THE TEACH YOURSELF BOOKS
EDITED BY LEONARD CUTTS

MECHANICS

TEACH YOURSELF

MECHANICS

By

P. ABBOTT, B.A.

THE ENGLISH UNIVERSITIES PRESS LTD
102 NEWGATE STREET
LONDON · E.C.1

First printed 1941
This impression 1964

Printed in Great Britain for the English Universities Press, Limited,
by Richard Clay and Company, Ltd., Bungay, Suffolk

INTRODUCTION

THIS book has been written designedly for the private student and especially for those who need to acquire a knowledge of the mechanical principles which underlie much of the work in many branches of industry and in the technical branches of the fighting forces. It is difficult in these troubled times to obtain the tuition provided by Scientific and Technical Institutions for such subjects as Mechanics. Nor is there any completely satisfactory substitute. Nevertheless the author hopes and believes that enough can be learnt from the present volume to be of very real practical use as an introduction to the subject. Like other volumes in the " Teach Yourself " series, it seeks to give such help as is possible to those students who are anxious to acquire a knowledge of the subject but must rely, in the main, on their own studies.

The difficulty is increased in such a subject when access is not possible to laboratories and apparatus. The view of the author of this book, founded on long experience, is that the approach to mechanics should be largely experimental. To a considerable extent the subject has been built up through centuries of human progress by experiment, often prompted by the needs of mankind. Experiment has preceded theory, as witness the discoveries of Archimedes, Torricelli and Galileo.

What is to take the place of this practical basis for the subject? In the early chapters of this book directions and descriptions are given of experiments with simple apparatus such as most students with a little ingenuity can construct or obtain. By this means the student is led to formulate some of the simple fundamental principles upon which the subject is built.

When the apparatus required is more complicated and cannot be obtained by the student it seems to the author that in many cases there is little value in the description of experiments which have been performed by others, with the numerical results which must be accepted without personal verification. It seems simpler and just as convincing to state the principles which are demonstrated by such experiments, leaving the verification for later study.

Mathematical proofs which involve a knowledge and experience of the subject which may be beyond the average student are omitted, the truth of the principles which they demonstrate being assumed.

Another important factor in a book of this kind is that of the amount of mathematical knowledge which may be assumed as being possessed by the average reader. The minimum amount required for the greater part of this volume is ordinary arithmetic, elementary algebra including the solution of quadratic equations with a knowledge of ratio, variation and a certain amount of fundamental geometry. In some sections of the book a knowledge of elementary trigonometry is essential. To assist the student cross references, when it seems desirable, are given to the appropriate sections in the companion book on Trigonometry in this series. In those cases in which practical drawing can be employed as an alternative to a trigonometrical solution, this is indicated.

Inevitable limitations of space have made it necessary to exclude many practical and technical applications of the principles evolved. It has been considered more profitable for private students, who in many cases are familiar with practical applications, that as much space as possible should be given to explanations of the theoretical aspects of the subject.

The examples to be worked by the student are designed to enable him to test his knowledge of the theorems on which they are based and to consolidate his knowledge of them. Academic exercises, depending for their solution mainly on mathematical ingenuity have been excluded.

The author desires to express his thanks to Mr. W. D. Hills, B.Sc. for permission to use diagrams 22 and 138 from his book on " Mechanics and Applied Mathematics," published by the University of London Press; also to

Messrs. Cussons for the use of blocks of some of the admirable apparatus which has been designed by them for use in teaching mechanics. The author is also indebted to Mr. C. E. Kerridge, B.Sc. for the use of the example on p. 207 from " National Certificate Mathematics," Vol. I, and to the University of London for their consent to the inclusion of a few of their Examination questions.

CONTENTS

CHAPTER V

COMPONENTS OF A FORCE, RESOLVED PARTS OF A FORCE

CHAPTER VI

TRIANGLE OF FORCES; POLYGON OF FORCES; LAMI'S THEOREM

CHAPTER VII

FRICTION

CHAPTER VIII

BODIES IN MOTION-VELOCITY

CHAPTER IX
ACCELERATION

CHAPTER X
NEWTON'S LAWS OF MOTION

CHAPTER XI
IMPULSE AND MOMENTUM ; WORK, ENERGY, POWER

CHAPTER XII
MACHINES

PARA.

CONTENTS

PAGE

CHAPTER XIII

COMPOSITION OF VELOCITIES ; RELATIVE VELOCITY

CHAPTER XIV

PROJECTILES

CHAPTER XV

DENSITY ; SPECIFIC GRAVITY

CHAPTER XVI

LIQUID PRESSURE

CHAPTER XVII

THE PRESSURE OF GASES

CHAPTER I

INTRODUCTORY

1. The Meaning of Mechanics.

THE word " Mechanics " is derived from a Greek word meaning " *contrivances* ", and this conveys some idea of the scope of the subject. Many of the " contrivances " and the fundamental principles underlying them form part of the instinctive heritage of the human race. Our body contains some of these contrivances, which, through long ages, have been adapted by Nature to our needs. If we lift a weight, or raise our feet from the ground in walking, we are employing " mechanisms " which are admirably adapted by nature for the purpose. A little child, in learning to stand and walk, is contriving by his experiments in balancing to solve problems which later will come up for our consideration in this book. Two children on a " see-saw " know the necessity of positioning themselves so that they may balance.

The principles of mechanics also enter vitally into the daily work of many, whether it is the bricklayer wheeling his barrow-load of bricks, the farmer pumping water from his well, or the aeronautical engineer designing an aeroplane. The scientific study of these principles through the ages has led to the complicated mechanisms of modern times, such as the steam-engine, the motor-car, or the machine-gun. It is important, therefore, that we should examine and learn to understand them, and that is the principal reason for studying mechanics.

2. Mechanics may be defined as the subject in which we study *the conditions under which objects around us move or are at rest*.

These two aspects of " rest " and " motion " of bodies have led to the division of the subject into two parts :

(1) **Statics**, which deals with bodies at rest.

(2) Dynamics, which is concerned with bodies in motion.

There is a further branch of the subject, which frequently has a volume to itself, viz. Hydrostatics, in which are studied the application to liquids and gases of those principles which have been examined for solids.

It will be noticed that the word " body " has been employed above, and it will continually enter into the work of this volume. The words " body " and " object " are meant to include all things which have weight—a term which we will examine more closely in the next paragraph. We assume, for the present, that all such " bodies " are " rigid "—i.e., different parts of them always retain the same relative positions.

3. Weight and Force.

Take a small heavy body, suspend it by a string, and hold the free end of this between the fingers. Now note that—

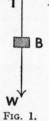

Fig. 1.

(1) In order to keep the body at rest, you must exert, by means of the muscles of your fingers and arm, what we call " force ". This force is exerted in an upward direction.

(2) This is necessary to counterbalance a force which is acting vertically downwards on the body, a force which we call the weight of the body.

This downward force, or weight, is called the " force of gravity ". It is the attraction which the earth exerts on all bodies, and tends to make them fall to the earth. We call it the weight of the body.

The weight of the body is therefore a force, which acts vertically downwards on it.

Returning to the experiment with the body suspended by a string, the diagram in Fig. 1 shows the method we employ to represent forces acting on a body.

B represents the body, and the straight lines indicate

the forces acting on it, the arrow-heads showing the directions of them. These are :

(1) The weight downwards, marked W.

(2) The pull upwards, exerted by the fingers through the string, and marked T.

Now, so long as the pull which you exert—viz., T— is equal to that of the weight, the body will remain at rest. If you increase your pull, the body will move upwards; if you decrease it, the body will move downwards. We may summarize this briefly as follows :

(1) If $T = W$, the body is at rest.

(2) If $T > W$, the body moves upwards.

(3) If $T < W$, the body moves downwards.

Thus an alteration in the forces acting on the body results in the body either being at rest or in motion.

It will be noticed that the term " force " has been used above before any definition of it has been given. The general meaning of the term is, however, familiar to everybody as one of the phenomena of everyday life; but it is desirable that it should be clear what the word implies, since it will constantly recur in subsequent chapters.

The simple experiment above and the conclusions drawn from it suggest the following definition.

Force is that which tends to produce motion in a body, to change that motion, or to keep the body at rest.

Force may have many different origins. It may be the result of muscular effort, it may be the force of gravity, the force of the wind, electrical force, the force of expanding steam, and so on.

4. Transmission of force. Tension.

The string employed in the above experiment is said to transmit the muscular force exerted by the fingers, to the body B, while the force of the weight of the object is transmitted to the fingers. The string is stretched by the action of these two forces and is said to be in tension under them.

This tension is the same throughout the string, and

so long as it is not greater than what is called the force of cohesion which keeps together the particles of the string, this will not break.

5. Equilibrium.

If a body is at rest under the action of forces it is said to be in equilibrium.

It follows that if two forces act on a body and there is equilibrium, the forces must be equal and opposite. Thus, as we have seen in the experiment above, if $T = W$ there is no motion and the body is in equilibrium.

The conditions under which a body can be in equilibrium under the action of more than two forces will be examined later.

6. The Measurement of a Force.

We have seen that the *weight of a body is the force with which the earth attracts it*. In measuring the magnitude of a force it is convenient to express it in terms of the weight of a certain number of lbs. For example, we may say that the magnitude of a certain force is 10 lbs. wt., of another 50 lbs. wt. The magnitude of a force is therefore expressed in terms of lbs. weight. It would clearly be incorrect to say that a force is 10 lbs. or 50 lbs.

7. A spring balance.

It is not possible by the use of muscular force to distinguish accurately between forces of different magnitudes. Thus in the experiment of a load suspended by a string we could detect that a load of 2 lbs. was considerably greater than that of 1 lb., but we could not tell how much greater.

It is therefore necessary to have more exact methods of measuring the magnitudes of forces, especially when dealing with forces which are not those of gravity and which do not act vertically downwards.

There are many methods of doing this, but the simplest and the one most commonly used is the **spring balance**. One of these is shown in Fig. 2. If you take a coiled spring and attach a weight of one lb., it will extend in length by a certain amount. Now, it can be demonstrated by experiment that the extension in the length of the spring is proportional to the magnitude of the force. If therefore a weight of 2 lbs. be attached to the spring, the extension in its length will be twice the extension for 1 lb.

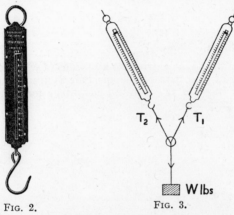

FIG. 2.   FIG. 3.

In this way it is possible to construct a scale by the side of the spring on which will be shown the magnitude of the force which produces a certain extension.

The spring balance can be used to measure force acting in any direction. Thus suppose a load of W lbs. is supported by two spring balances, as shown in Fig. 3, then the tension in each string, shown as T_1 and T_2 in the figure, can be measured on the corresponding spring balance.

CHAPTER II

THE LEVER

8. Machines.

A MACHINE is a contrivance by means of which a force applied at one part of the machine is transmitted to another in order to secure an advantage for some particular purpose.

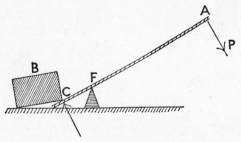

FIG. 4.

For example, suppose I wish to raise a heavy stone indicated in Fig. 4 by B. I insert an iron bar under one edge at C and pivot it on a suitable object, such as a stone, at F. By the application of a comparatively small force, P, at A, this force is transmitted to C, acts upwards, and raises the stone.

The bar is thus a contrivance by means of which it is possible to transmit an applied force to secure the advantage of a larger force acting at another point.

The rod is a simple example of a lever, which is probably one of the earliest machines to be used by man, and today, in various forms and combinations, is the most widely used of all machines.

We must now proceed to examine the principles underlying it, for it is only when these are understood that progress may be made in developing the uses of the machine.

9. The principles of the lever.

The student can easily discover the mechanical principles of a lever by a few simple experiments.

A long bar is the essential thing for a lever. We will therefore begin by experimenting with a long rod or bar which is graduated in inches or centimetres, in order to facilitate the experiments. A yard-stick is very suitable. It will be necessary to have some means of pivoting the rod, so that it may turn about the point of the

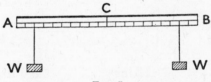

Fig. 5.

pivoting. This could be done by boring holes, with smooth interior surfaces, then passing a knitting-needle, or something similar, through a hole. The needle is then supported in some way.

We will begin by pivoting the stick in the middle. Let *AB* (Fig. 5) represent such a bar and *C* the centre hole about which it is pivoted. If this is done accurately the bar will rest in a horizontal position. In this form the lever is a simple balance, and if equal weights, *W*, are suspended at equal distances from the centre, the rod will be in equilibrium. It should be noted that the weight near *B* tends to turn the rod about *C* in a clockwise direction, while that near *A* tends to turn the rod in an anti-clockwise direction.

The turning effects of these two weights, each of which is a force acting vertically downwards, balance one another and so the equilibrium is not disturbed.

10. Turning moments.

The effect of hanging a weight at any point on one arm of the lever is to cause the lever to turn about the point of support. We must now therefore investigate how this turning effect is affected by :

(1) The **magnitude** of the weight hung on.
(2) The **distance** of the weight from the pivot, called the **fulcrum**.
(3) The **position** of the fulcrum.

First let us consider experiments in which we vary the magnitudes of the weights and their distances from

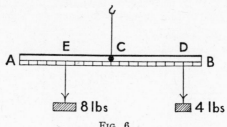

FIG. 6.

the fulcrum, which we will still keep at the centre of the lever.

Let a weight of **4 lbs.** be suspended at D (Fig. 6) 10 in. from C, the fulcrum. Let this be balanced by 8 lbs. placed on the other arm. It will be found that to balance the 4 lbs. we must place the 8 lbs. at E, 5 in. from C.

Thus   4 lbs. acting 10 in. from C on one arm
balances 8   ,,   5   ,, C ,, the other arm.
In other words—

The turning effect in a clockwise direction of 4 lbs. acting 10 in. from C balances the turning effect in an anti-clockwise direction of 8 lbs. acting 5 in. from C.

It will be noticed that the products of weight and distance in the two cases, viz. 4×10 and 8×5, are equal.

This product of force (or weight) and distance is called the turning moment of the force.

We further notice in this case that when the turning moments balance about the fulcrum, they are equal. Similar experiments in which the weights and distances are varied lead to the conclusion that this is true generally.

In these experiments the fulcrum or pivot is at the centre of the lever.

We must now try similar experiments when the fulcrum is in any position. This time instead of suspending the bar it is balanced about a knife-edge at F (the fulcrum).

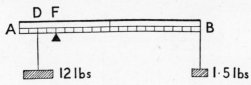

FIG. 7.

Let the lever, AB (Fig. 7), be 20 in. long. Let the fulcrum, F, be 4 in. from A.

A weight of 12 lbs. is hung at D, 2 in. from F.

If we experiment to find what weight placed at B, the end of the lever, will balance this, it will be found that 1·5 lbs. is needed.

Thus   12 lbs. at 2 in. from F is balanced by
       1·5   „   16 „   „ F.

The turning moment (clockwise) of

$$1\text{·}5 \text{ lbs. at } B = 1\text{·}5 \times 16 = 24.$$

The turning moment (anti-clockwise) of

$$12 \text{ lbs. at } D = 12 \times 2 = 24.$$

The turning moments of the two weights are equal and opposite.

Similar experiments with varying weights and distances and different positions of the fulcrum lead to the same conclusion, viz.—

When the turning moments of two forces about the fulcrum of a lever are equal and opposite, the lever is in equilibrium.

The converse is also true.

Note.—When turning moments are thus calculated with regard to the fulcrum at F, we say that " we take moments (or turning moments) about F ".

In the previous experiments, and the conclusions drawn from them, we have considered the case in which one weight only was placed on each arm. To complete the investigation experiments should be made

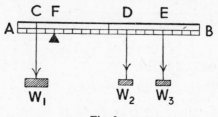

Fig. 8.

to discover what happens if more than one weight is acting.

We can proceed as follows :

Let a bar, AB, as before, rest on a fulcrum at F (Fig. 8).

Let three weights, W_1, W_2, W_3, be suspended from the bar at C, D, and E. Let d_1, d_2, d_3 be their distances from the fulcrum.

Let these weights be so arranged that the bar is in horizontal equilibrium—*i.e.*, it balances about F and remains horizontal.

Now W_2 and W_3 exert a clockwise turning movement about F.

While W_1 exerts an anti-clockwise effect.

If there is equilibrium these must balance—*i.e.*, the

clockwise turning moment must equal the anti-clockwise moment.

$$\therefore \quad (W_1 \times d_1) = (W_2 \times d_2) + (W_3 \times d_3).$$

This should be verified experimentally by actual weights and measured distances.

11. Relation between weights and distances.

Let AB be a bar with the fulcrum, F, at its centre (Fig. 9).

Let W_1 and W_2 be unequal weights hung on the bar so that the bar rests in horizontal equilibrium.

Let d_1 and d_2 be the respective distances from F.

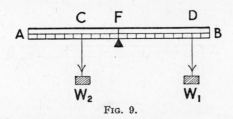

Fig. 9.

Since there is equilibrium, the clockwise turning moments equal the anti-clockwise.

$$\therefore \quad W_1 \times d_1 = W_2 \times d_2.$$

This can be written in the form :

$$\frac{W_1}{W_2} = \frac{d_2}{d_1}.$$

12. The weight of the lever.

We have hitherto disregarded the weight of the lever, assuming the bar to be " light ", so that its weight does not materially affect the conclusions. But if the lever used is not light, discrepancies will have appeared in the results of the experiments.

It must first be noted that the weight will, of course, act vertically downwards. Early mathematicians as-

sumed it as axiomatic that the whole of the weight
could be considered as acting at the centre of the lever,
provided that the lever is uniform. This is confirmed
by the fact that it can be supported in horizontal
equilibrium at its centre. If it be thus suspended by
means of a spring balance it will be found that the
balance registers the whole weight of the lever which
must therefore act at the point of suspension.

The following experiment will serve to demonstrate
this, as well as to illustrate our previous conclusions.

Suspend the lever from a point, O (*see* Fig. 10).

Suspend also a weight, W, at A, of such a magnitude
that the rod rests in horizontal equilibrium.

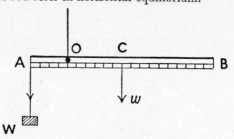

Fig. 10.

Then, from our previous conclusions, the anti-clockwise moment of W acting at A must be counterbalanced
by the weight of the lever, which, as the moment must
be clockwise, must act somewhere along OB.

Let the point at which it acts be x ins. from O.

Then by the conclusions of § 10,
the moment of W = moment of the weight of the lever.

Let this weight be w.

Then $$w \times x = W \times OA.$$

∴ $$x = \frac{W \times OA}{w}.$$

Now OA can be measured and W and w are known.

∴ x can be calculated, and so we find the distance
from O at which the weight must act.

From the experiment you will find that $x = OC$, where C is the centre of the lever.

Thus the weight of the lever can be considered as acting at the centre of the lever.

The point at which the force of gravity on the lever— *i.e.*, its weight—acts, is called the **Centre of Gravity** of the rod. If the lever is not uniform the centre of gravity will not be at the centre of the lever, but its position can be found by using the above method.

The term " Centre of Gravity " is introduced now as it arises naturally out of the experiments performed, but the full consideration of it is postponed until Chapter III.

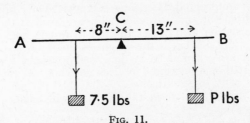

Fig. 11.

Exercise 1

1. A light rod, AB, 30 in. long, is pivoted at its centre, C, and a load of 8 lbs. is hung 12 in. from C.

    (*a*) Where on CB should a load of 15 lbs. be placed to balance this?

    (*b*) What load should be placed 10 in. from C to preserve equilibrium?

2. Fig. 11 shows a light rod, AB, of length 36 in. pivoted at its centre, C. Loads are hung as indicated.

    (*a*) What is the value of P?

    (*b*) If the 7·5 lbs. were placed at A what would then be the value of P?

    (*c*) If a weight of 5 lbs. were hung at B, what weight must be placed 12 in. from A to preserve equilibrium?

3. A light rod, AB, 40 in. long, has a fulcrum at its centre. Loads of 4·5 lbs. and 2·5 lbs. are attached on one arm at distances 8 in. and 5 in. respectively from the fulcrum. Where must a single load of 4 lbs. be placed on the other arm to preserve equilibrium?

4. A light rod 4 ft. long balances about a fulcrum 15 in. from one end. A load of 18 oz. is placed on the shorter arm and 7 in. from the fulcrum.

(a) What weight placed 30 in. from the fulcrum on the other arm will balance it?

(b) Where must a load of 5 oz. be placed for the same purpose?

5. A uniform rod, 24 in. long, is supported on a fulcrum 8 in. from one end. A load of $1\frac{3}{4}$ oz. placed at the end of the shorter arm causes the rod to rest in horizontal equilibrium. What is the weight of the rod?

6. A uniform rod 36 in. long and weighing 4 oz. is supported on a fulcrum 5 in. from one end. At this end a load of 12 lbs. is attached. What load placed on the other arm, 25 in. from the fulcrum, will balance this weight?

7. It is desired to raise a weight of 300 lbs. placed at the end of a uniform iron bar, 4 ft. long and weighing 18 lbs. To effect this a fulcrum is placed 4 in. from this end, and the bar pivoted on it. What effort must be exerted at the other end of the bar, so that the weight can just be moved?

8. A uniform bar 36 in. long, and of unknown weight, rests on a fulcrum 6 in. from one end. It is in equilibrium when loads of 6 lbs. and 36 lbs. are hung at the ends of the bar.

(a) What is the weight of the bar?

(b) What load at the end of the long arm will balance a load of 24 lbs. at the end of the short arm?

9. A uniform iron bar, 48 in. long and of weight 5 lbs., rests on a fulcrum 8 in. from one end. On the other arm loads of 3 lbs. each are hung at every 10 in. from

the fulcrum. What load at the end of the short arm will preserve horizontal equilibrium?

10. A heavy uniform bar is 30 in. long and weighs 2 lbs. A weight of 3 lbs. is placed at one end, and at the other a weight of 5 lbs. At what point on the bar must it be supported so that it balances and does not turn?

---

13. Pressure on the fulcrum. Resultant force.

In the previous experiments weights have been hung on a rod which was supported at the fulcrum; conse-

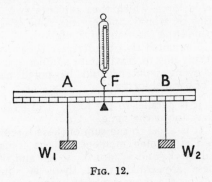

FIG. 12.

quently there is a pressure on the fulcrum. To ascertain the amount of this pressure the following experiment may be performed.

Let a bar (Fig. 12) be loaded with two weights, W_1 and W_2, placed so that there is equilibrium about a fulcrum, F. Replace the fulcrum by a hook attached to a spring balance and let this be raised slightly so that it takes the weight of the whole system. If there is still equilibrium, then the spring balance will register the pressure which was formerly borne by the fulcrum.

Taking the reading of the spring balance, you will find, as you probably expected, that it is equal to the sum of the weights—*i.e.*, to $W_1 + W_2$. If the rod is not a light one the weight of the lever will also be borne by the fulcrum, or the spring balance which replaces it.

Let   R be the pressure recorded.
Then $R = W_1 + W_2$.

If other weights be placed on the lever, equilibrium being preserved, the pressure on the fulcrum is increased by these.

It is clear that if the two weights or forces, W_1 and W_2, were replaced at F by a single weight or force, R, equal to their sum, the spring balance would register the same amount as before; the effect on the fulcrum, F, would be the same.

The single force which thus replaces two separate forces acting on a body, and has the same effect on the body, is called the resultant of the forces.

It should be noted that the forces represented by W_1 and W_2, being due to gravity, are parallel forces.

The following points should be noted about the resultant of parallel forces.

(1) It is parallel to the forces it can replace and its direction is the same.

(2) It is equal to the sum of these forces.

(3) The turning moments of the forces represented by W_1 and W_2 are $W_1 \times AF$ and $W_2 \times BF$. These are equal, since there is equilibrium. Therefore, the moments of the forces about F, the point at which the resultant acts, are equal.

(4) Since $W_1 \times AF = W_2 \times BF$

$$\therefore \qquad \frac{AF}{BF} = \frac{W_2}{W_1}.$$

$\therefore$ the point at which the resultant of the two parallel forces acts divides the distance between them in the inverse ratio of their magnitudes.

14. Centre of force.

The converse of the above is also true—viz., if two parallel forces represented by W_1 and W_2 act on a bar at A and B (see Fig. 13), it is possible to find a point,

F, between them so that

$$\frac{AF}{FB} = \frac{W_2}{W_1},$$

and $\qquad W_1 \times AF = W_2 \times FB.$

But these are the moments of W_1 and W_2 about F.

∴ it is possible to find a point so that the moments about it of the two forces are equal and opposite and there is therefore equilibrium.

Such a point is called **the centre of force**, and at this point the resultant acts.

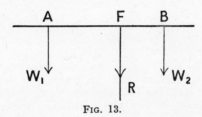

FIG. 13.

15. Bars resting on two supports.

The principles that have been established in the preceding pages may be extended to the case of loaded rods, bars, or beams which rest on two supports. In problems arising from this arrangement it is important to be able to calculate the thrust of the supports on the bar or beam, or, conversely, of the thrusts on the supports. The practical applications are very important. The following is a description of an experiment by means of which these thrusts may be found practically.

In Fig. 14, AB represents a heavy uniform bar, or beam, resting on two supports at C and D. These may be attached to compression balances, or the bar may be suspended from spring balances fixed at these points, as was shown in § 13.

Let loads W_1 and W_2 be suspended from two points.

Let w be the weight of the bar, acting at the centre of it.

If the recorded pressures registered at C and D are examined it will be found that—

total pressures at C and $D = W_1 + W_2 + w$.

This was to be expected, since these two supports must take the whole of the downward forces, due to

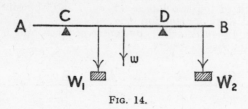

FIG. 14.

gravity. It will be seen, however, from the readings of the two balances that this pressure is not divided evenly between the two supports. Our problem is to discover how, in any given instance, these may be calculated.

We will first consider the simple case of a heavy bar,

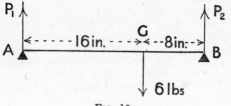

FIG. 15.

in which the centre of gravity is not at the centre of the bar and no additional loads are placed on it.

(a) Experimental method.

Let AB (Fig. 15) be a heavy bar 24 in. long, weight 6 lbs., and supported at A and B.

The centre of gravity is not at the centre of the rod but known to be at G, where $AG = 16$ in., $GB = 8$ in.

Let P_1, P_2 be the pressures at A and B.

Consider the forces acting on the bar AB. These are:

> downward—the weight of the bar, 6 lbs.
> upward—$P_1 + P_2$ (equal and opposite to thrust on the supports).

Since there is equilibrium, these must be equal.

$$\therefore \qquad P_1 + P_2 = 6.$$

Reading the balances at A and B we find:

$$P_2 = 4, \; P_1 = 2,$$

confirming the conclusion already reached that

$$P_1 + P_2 = 6.$$

We note that

$$P_2 : P_1 = 2 : 1 = 16 : 8 = AG : GB.$$

Thus we find from the experiment that **the pressures on the supports are inversely proportional to the distances from G.**

This can be confirmed by similar experiments.

(b) Use of principles of moments.

Since P_1 and P_2 represent the pressures of the bar on A and B, equal and opposite thrusts must be exerted on the bar, as is stated above, since there is equilibrium at these points.

Suppose the support at A were removed. The bar would turn about the other support at B, and we could regard the bar as a lever, just on the point of turning about B.

The bar is then subject to the turning moments about B of:

> (1) the weight at G—anti-clockwise.
> (2) P_1 at A—clockwise.

The thrust P_2 at B has no effect on rotation about B. These turning moments must be equal.

$$\therefore \qquad\qquad P_1 \times 24 = 6 \times 8.$$
$$\therefore \qquad\qquad\qquad P_1 = 2 \text{ lbs. wt.}$$

Similarly, if we imagine the bar on the point of turning about A the turning moments are :

        (1) $P_2 \times 24$—anti-clockwise
        (2) 6×16—clockwise
$$\therefore \qquad\qquad P_2 \times 24 = 6 \times 16$$
and $\qquad\qquad\qquad P_2 = 4 \text{ lbs. wt.}$

The methods adopted in this case are also applicable when loads are attached to the bar. This is illustrated in the following example :

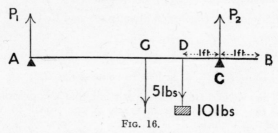

Fig. 16.

16. Worked example.

A uniform heavy bar AB, of length 6 ft. and weight 5 lbs., is supported at one end A and also at C, which is 1 ft. from B. A load of 10 lbs. is suspended at D, which is 1 ft. from C. Find the pressures on the supports at A and C.

Fig. 16 represents the rod AB.

As the rod is uniform, the centre of gravity is at the centre, G, of the rod.

Let $P_1 =$ upward thrust at A.
$\therefore \quad P_2 = \qquad ,, \qquad\qquad ,, \quad C.$

These are equal and opposite to the pressures of the bar on the supports at A and C.

Forces acting on the bar.

        (1) Weight, 5 lbs., downward at G.
        (2) Load, 10 lbs.   ,, D.
        (3) P_1 upward at A.
        (4) P_2 ,, C.

Now, suppose that the support at A were to be removed so that the bar begins to rotate about C. We find the turning moments of the forces which tend to make the bar rotate about C. They are :

$P_1 \times 5$—clockwise.
$(5 \times 2) + (10 \times 1)$—anti-clockwise.

As there is equilibrium about C, these must be equal.

$$\therefore \qquad P_1 \times 5 = (5 \times 2) + (10 \times 1).$$
$$\therefore \qquad 5P_1 = 20.$$
and $\qquad P_1 = 4$ lbs. wt.

Similarly, equating moments about A

Clockwise. Anti-Clockwise.
$$P_2 \times 5 = (5 \times 3) + (10 \times 4).$$
$$\therefore \qquad 5P_2 = 55$$
and $\qquad P_2 = 11$ lbs. wt.

We may check by noting that since there is equilibrium the forces acting vertically upwards must be equal to those acting vertically downwards. We have :

Upward $\quad P_1 + P_2 = 4 + 11 = 15$ lbs. wt.,
downward $\quad 5$ lbs. $+ 10$ lbs. $= 15$ lbs. wt.

Exercise 2.

1. A uniform bar, 4 ft. long, weighing 10 lbs., is supported at one end and also 6 in. from the other end. Find the load carried on the supports.

2. A weight of 8 stone is hung on a uniform wooden pole 5 ft. long and weighing 7 lbs. It is then carried by two men, one at each end of the pole. It is so arranged that the position of the weight on the pole is 2 ft. from the stronger man. What weight will be borne by each of the men?

3. A uniform beam 6 ft. long and weighing 20 lbs. is supported at each end. Loads of 50 lbs. and 60 lbs. are carried at distances of 1 ft. and 4 ft. respectively from one end. Find the load on each support.

4. A uniform plank, AB, 8 ft. long and weighing 10 lbs., is supported between two steel pegs, C and D,

B—MECH.

arranged as shown in Fig. 17, one, C, at one end of the plank, and the other, D, 1 ft. from the end. The plank carries a load of 20 lbs., suspended 1 ft. from the end B. Find the thrusts on the pegs.

5. A uniform wooden plank weighing 20 lbs., and 16 ft. long, is placed symmetrically on two supports 12 ft. apart. A load of 80 lbs. is attached to one end and 100 lbs. to the other. What is the pressure on the supports?

6. A uniform bar 2 ft. long weighs 2 lb. and is supported at its two ends. A 7-lbs. weight is hung from the bar, 6 in. from one end, and a 4-lbs. weight 9 in. from the other end. Find the pressures on the two supports.

7. A heavy uniform beam, AB, weighing 1½ tons, is supported at one end, A, and at a point C, one quarter

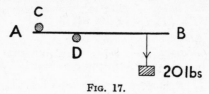

FIG. 17.

the length of the beam from the other end, B. A load of ½ ton rests on the end B. What force acts on the support A?

8. A plank 16 ft. long and weighing 30 lbs. rests on supports at each end. A man weighing 12 stones stands on the plank 4 ft. from one end. What is the pressure on each of the ends?

17. Orders of levers.

As we have seen, a lever, in addition to a bar or rod, involves:

(1) A load.
(2) A fulcrum.
(3) An applied force.

The relative positions which these may occupy on the lever may vary. Hitherto, in the examples which we have examined, the position of the fulcrum has been between the load and the applied force. As the positions of these are altered we have different types of levers. Three arrangements are possible, and these, since the time of Archimedes, have been called the **three orders of levers.**

The relative positions in these orders are shown in Fig. 18.

18. The principle of moments in the three orders.

The principles established for levers of the first order apply to the other orders and may be verified experi-

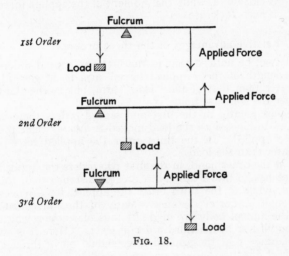

Fig. 18.

mentally by the student. In particular the principle of moments is very important, and it is worth while considering its application in the three orders. The principle was :

When the lever is in equilibrium the turning moments of the forces which tend to produce motion in a clockwise direction about the fulcrum are equal to those of the forces tending to produce motion in an anti-clockwise direction.

In applying this principle to the three orders it may be noted that:

(1) In the **first order**, since the load and applied force act on opposite sides of the fulcrum, one will naturally be clockwise and the other anti-clockwise, though they both **act in the same direction**.

(2) In the **second and third orders**, if one is to be clockwise and the other anti-clockwise they **must act in opposite directions**. On examining Fig. 18 it will be seen that in levers of the second and third orders the **moment of the load about the fulcrum is clockwise, while the moment of the applied force is anti-clockwise**.

19. Relative advantages of the three orders.

It will be noticed that in the first and second orders the length of the " applied force " arm is, in general, greater than that of the "load" arm, but in the third order the converse holds.

Consequently in the first and second orders there is an advantage, since the load moved is greater than the force applied. In the third order the applied force is greater than the load.

On the other hand, in the first two orders the applied force has to move through a greater distance than the load, while in the third order the applied force moves through a shorter distance. Many of the movements in the human body are made by muscular action which is applied as in the third order of levers. Here it is an advantage that the applied force should move through a short distance.

20. Practical examples of levers.

The following are a few examples of the practical applications of levers in daily life.

First order.

A balance, crowbar (with fulcrum arranged as in Fig. 19(a), a poker (pivoted on a bar), a pair of scissors or pliers (double lever hinged), steel-yard, pump handle (Fig. 19b).

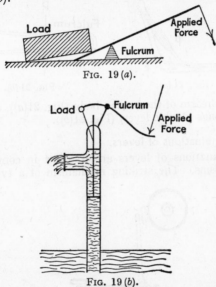

FIG. 19 (a).

FIG. 19 (b).

Second order.   Third order

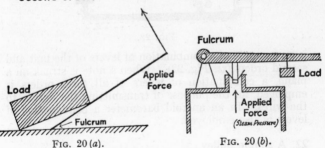

FIG. 20 (a).   FIG. 20 (b).

A crowbar (with fulcrum on ground as in Fig. 20(a)), a wheelbarrow, pair of nutcrackers (double-hinged), oar of a boat, a safety valve lever (Fig. 20b).

Third order.

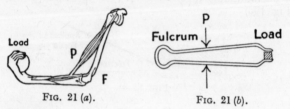

Fig. 21 (a).

Fig. 21 (b).

The forearm of the human body (Fig. 21(a)), a pair of sugar-tongs (double lever) (Fig. 21(b)).

21. Combinations of levers.

Combinations of levers are frequent in complicated mechanisms. The striking mechanism of a typewriter

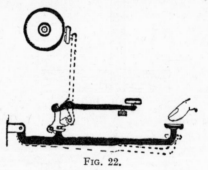

Fig. 22.

is an example of a combination of levers of the first and second orders (*see* Fig. 22). When a note is struck on a piano, a combination of levers of all three orders is employed, for the purpose of transmitting the action to the wires. In an aneroid barometer a combination of levers is also employed.

22. A simple pulley.

The pulley is another very useful machine. In its simplest form it consists of a wheel with outer rim grooved to permit of a rope travelling round it (Fig. 23).

The axle of the wheel is attached to a fixed beam or other support. In this form the pulley is employed merely to change the direction of an applied force.

Thus in Fig. 23 it will be seen that a weight, W, can be pulled *upwards* by a force, P, acting *downwards* on the rope which is attached to W and passes round the pulley.

If the pulley is assumed to be " smooth "—*i.e.*, there is no friction—then the tension in the rope is the same throughout and $P = W$.

It should be noted that since there is a pull, P, in the rope on each side of the pulley, the total force acting on the pulley is $2P$.

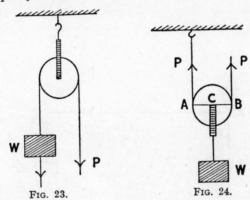

Fig. 23.   Fig. 24.

A movable pulley.

In the arrangement shown in Fig. 24 the pulley is a movable one. A rope is fixed to a beam and passes round a travelling pulley, to the axle of which the weight, W, to be lifted is attached.

Let the applied force be P. Then the tension in the rope is P throughout.

∴ the pulley is sustained by two cords in each of which the tension is P.

∴ the weight supported is $2P$.

∴ $$W = 2P.$$

This takes no account of the weight of the pulley. If this be considerable and equal to w,

then $$W + w = 2P.$$

The above relation between P and W may be obtained by applying the principle of moments.

AB, the diameter of the pulley, may be regarded as a moving lever, since as the pulley rotates, one diameter is instantly replaced by another diameter.

If moments be taken about A, we have P acting at B and W at C.

$$P \times AB = W \times AC.$$
but $$AB = 2AC.$$
$$\therefore \quad W = 2P$$

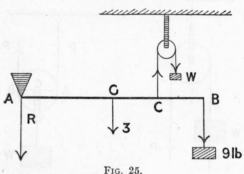

FIG. 25.

23. Worked examples.

Example 1. *An iron bar AB, 4 ft. long and weighing 3 lbs., turns about a fulcrum at A (Fig. 25). At B a weight of 9 lbs. is hung. At a point, C, 1 ft. from B a cord is attached to the rod and is passed vertically upwards over a smooth pulley fixed to a beam. To this cord a load of W lbs. is fixed to perserve equilibrium. Find W and the pressure on the rod at the fulcrum.*

The tension in the cord passing over the pulley is the same throughout.

$$\therefore \quad \text{at } C, W \text{ lbs. wt. acts upward.}$$

Let R = pressure on the rod at the fulcrum.

To find W take moments about A.
By doing this the unknown pressure R is eliminated.
Then

Anti-clockwise.		Clockwise.
$W \times 3$	$=$	$(3 \times 2) + (9 \times 4)$.
$\therefore$ $3W$	$=$	$6 + 36 = 42$
$\therefore$ W	$=$	14 lbs. wt.

To find R take moments about C.

Anti-clockwise.	Clockwise.
$(R \times 3) + (3 \times 1) =$	9×1.
$\therefore$ $3R + 3 =$	9
$R =$	2

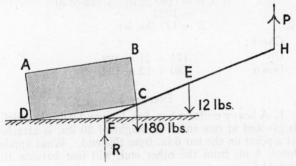

FIG. 26.

As a check:
Upward force $W = 14$.
Downward force $2 + 3 + 9 = 14$.

Example 2. *A uniformly loaded rectangular box weighing 360 lbs. is lying with a face on horizontal ground. A uniform crowbar, 6 ft. long and weighing 12 lbs., is inserted 6 in. under it in a direction perpendicular to one edge and at the mid point of the edge. Find what force must be applied at the other end of the bar so that the box may be just tilted. Find also the pressure of the bar on the ground.*

Fig. 26 represents a vertical section through the symmetrical centre of the box.

The bar, FH, when just on the point of tilting will sustain at C, the point of contact, 6 in. from F, a pressure which will be half the weight of the box—*i.e.*, 180 lbs.—the other half being borne by the other edge at D.

Let P be upward force applied at H.

Take moments about F for the equilibrium of the bar.

Anti-clockwise.   Clockwise.
$$P \times 6 = (180 \times \tfrac{1}{2}) + (12 \times 3)$$
$$= 126$$
$$\therefore \qquad P = 21 \text{ lbs. wt.}$$

Let R be pressure of ground on the bar.

Take moments about H for the equilibrium of the bar.

Then $\qquad R \times 6 = (180 \times 5\tfrac{1}{2}) + (12 \times 3)$
$$= 1026.$$
$$\therefore \qquad R = 171 \text{ lbs. wt.}$$

Check:

Up $171 + 21 = 192.$
Down $180 + 12 = 192.$

Exercise 3.

1. A heavy uniform bar, 5 ft. long and 2 lbs. in weight, is pivoted at one end. A weight of 30 lbs. is attached at a point on the bar 6 in. from this end. What applied force, 4 in. from the other end, will just balance this weight?

2. A crowbar, 4 ft. long, has one end pivoted on the ground. At a distance of 8 in. from this end a load exerts a force equal to the weight of one ton. Disregarding the weight of the crowbar, what force must be applied at the other end so as just to raise the load? What will be the thrust of the ground on the bar at its end?

3. A uniform bar, 3 ft. long and weighing 2 lb., is pivoted at one end. At the other end a load of 6 lbs. is placed. What upward force applied at a point 9 in. from this will produce equilibrium? What will be the pressure on the fulcrum?

4. A man pulls an oar 7 ft. long with the end of the handle 2 ft. from the rowlock. Find the ratios of the

pull at the end of the handle by the oarsman, the resistance of the boat to the oar at the rowlock, and the resistance of the water acting at the end of the oar.

5. A rectangular block of stone, weight 320 lbs., lies horizontally on the ground. A crowbar, of length 5 ft. and weight 15 lbs. is pushed under the block to a distance of 1 ft. What force applied at the other end of the crowbar will just tilt the block?

6. In a pair of nut-crackers a nut is placed $\frac{3}{4}$ in. from the hinge and the pressure applied at the handles is estimated to act at a distance of 6 in. from the hinge, and to be equivalent to 7 lbs. wt. What is the pressure applied to the nut?

7. A uniform heavy plank, 32 ft. long and weighing 80 lbs., projects 8 ft. horizontally from the top of a cliff. How far can a man weighing 160 lbs. move along the plank before it tips up?

8. In a safety-valve (*see* Fig. 20(*b*)) the distance between the fulcrum and the centre of the piston is 3 in., and the area of the surface of the valve is 3 sq. in. The lever is 8 in. long and has a load of 60 lb. at the end of it. Find the pressure of the steam per sq. in. when the valve is just beginning to move upwards.

9. A pump handle is 3 ft. 6 in. long from the pivot to the end. The pivot is 3·5 in. from the point where it is attached to the plunging rod. A force of 20 lbs. wt. is applied at the end of the handle. What force is applied to the plunging rod?

10. A uniform iron bar is 8 ft. long and weighs 10 lbs. It is pivoted at one end and a load of 40 lbs. is placed 1 ft. from the pivot. What force applied at the other end of the bar will just support this load?

CHAPTER III

CENTRE OF GRAVITY

24. Centre of parallel forces.

In the previous chapter it was shown that if two parallel forces represented by weights acted on a bar so that their opposing moments about an axis on the bar were equal, the bar was in equilibrium.

It was also seen that the two forces could be replaced by a single force, equal to their sum and parallel to them, acting at the axis. This force is called the **resultant of the forces**, and the point at which it acts is called the **centre of force**.

This principle may be extended to any number of forces.

Suppose that P_1, P_2, P_3 are parallel forces.

Let R_1 be the resultant of P_1 and P_2.

Then
$$R_1 = P_1 + P_2.$$

R_1 acts at a point which divides the distance between P_1 and P_2 in the ratio $P_2 : P_1$.

Now, R_1 and P_3 being parallel forces, the resultant of these can be found. Let R be the resultant.

Then $\quad R = R_1 + P_3 = P_1 + P_2 + P_3.$

It acts at a point between R_1 and P_3 which divides the distance between them in the ratio of $P_3 + P_2 : P_1$.

This is the point where R, the resultant of P_1, P_2, and P_3, acts, and is the centre of force of the system.

This may be extended to any number of forces.

When the forces acting are due to gravity, the centre of them is called the centre of gravity of the system.

Now, any solid body can be considered as composed of a large number of particles upon each of which the force of gravity acts. All these forces are parallel, and their resultant, expressed by the weight of the body, acts at the centre of these forces, which is therefore the centre of gravity of the body, thus:

The centre of gravity of a body is the point through which the resultant of the earth's pull upon the body passes and at which the weight of the body can be considered as acting.

25. To find the centre of gravity of a number of particles.

Let A and B (Fig. 27) be two particles of weights W_1 and W_2.

By the principle of § 24 the C.G. of these is at G_1 on the straight line joining them where

$$\frac{AG_1}{BG_1} = \frac{W_2}{W_1}.$$

∴ as we have seen, we can regard $W_1 + W_2$ as acting at G_1.

Let C be a third particle of weight W_3.

Then the C.G. of $W_1 + W_2$ at G_1 and W_3 at C lies at G on the straight line joining G_1C.

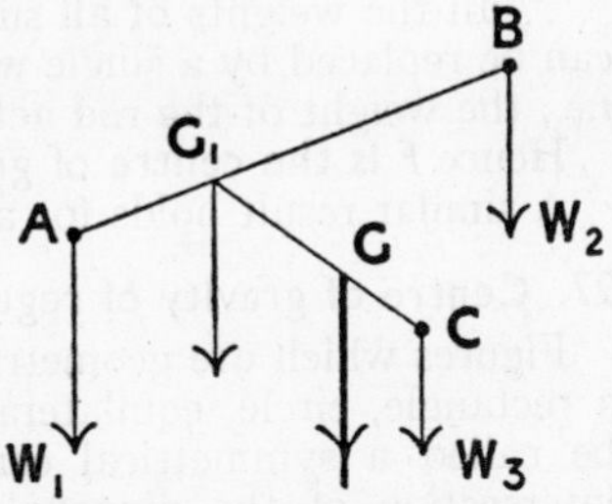

Fig. 27.

Where

$$\frac{CG}{G_1G} = \frac{W_1 + W_2}{W_3}.$$

The point G is therefore the centre of gravity of the three particles, and their resultant $W_1 + W_2 + W_3$ can be considered as acting at it.

26. Centre of gravity of a uniform rod.

We have assumed that a uniform rod can be balanced about its centre point, and experience shows that it can be supported in equilibrium by resting it on a fulcrum at this point. This implies that the effect of the force of gravity upon the parts of the rod on the two sides of the fulcrum is the same.

Let CD (Fig. 28) represent a uniform rod, and let A and B be two small equal portions of the rod situated at equal distances from the fulcrum F, at the centre of the rod.

Moments of these pieces about the fulcrum must be equal.

∴ they could be represented by a single force equal to their sum, acting at F.

The same reasoning applies to all such pieces throughout the equal arms.

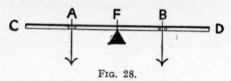

FIG. 28.

∴ all the weights of all such parts in these two arms can be replaced by a single weight, equal to their sum—*i.e.*, the weight of the rod acting at F.

Hence F is the centre of gravity of the rod.

A similar result holds for a narrow rectangular strip.

27. Centre of gravity of regular geometrical figures.

Figures which are geometrically symmetrical, such as a rectangle, circle, equilateral triangle, have what may be called a symmetrical centre, as, for example, the intersection of the diagonals of a rectangle. Such a point will be the centre of gravity of the figures, if uniform, since the forces of gravity will balance about it.

28. Experimental determination of the centre of gravity.

If a body be suspended from a point near one of its boundaries it will remain at rest when the point of support of the string lies vertically above the centre of gravity. In this way only can the principle of balance of turning moments be satisfied. This enables us to obtain experimentally the centre of gravity in certain cases.

The easiest object to experiment with is a flat uniform piece of cardboard, of any shape, such as is suggested by Fig. 29.

Pierce it near a rim (A in Fig. 29) with a fine needle, and stick this on a vertical board or paper. From this needle suspend a fine thread with a small weight attached and let it hang vertically. Mark two points on the straight line formed where the line touches the board, and draw the straight line AG.

Then the centre of gravity must lie on AG.

Take a second point B, repeat the experiment, and obtain the straight line BG. The centre of gravity must also lie on BG.

∴ the centre of gravity lies at G, the intersection of the two straight lines.

If the cardboard or other lamina has a perceptible thickness and is uniform, the centre of gravity will lie half-way between the two surfaces, underneath the point G.

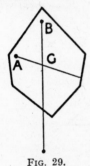

FIG. 29.

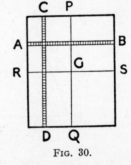

FIG. 30.

For obvious reasons, this method of finding the C.G. cannot be employed with solid bodies, but it should be remembered that when *any* body is suspended at a point and remains permanently at rest, the C.G. lies vertically below this point.

29. Centre of gravity of a rectangular lamina.

The C.G. of a rectangle will be the intersection of the diagonals (§ 27), since it is a symmetrical geometrical figure. But we employ this shaped lamina to demonstrate a very useful method of finding the C.G.

The rectangle can be considered as being composed of a large number of narrow rectangles such as AB (Fig. 30), all parallel to a pair of opposite sides. The C.G. of

AB is at the centre of the strip as shown in § 25. The C.G.s of all such strips must therefore lie along the straight line *PQ*, which joins the middle points of all the strips, and *P* and *Q*, the mid points of the opposite sides.

Similarly, the rectangle can be considered as made up of strips such as *CD*, parallel to the other pair of sides. The C.G. of all such strips will lie along *RS*, which joins the mid points.

∴ the C.G. lies at *G*, the intersection of *PQ* and *RS*. This point *G* is also the intersection of the diagonals.

Similarly we may find the C.G.s of a square, a parallelogram, and a rhombus.

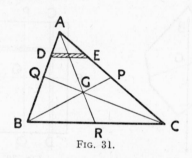

Fig. 31.

30. Centre of gravity of a triangular lamina.

The method is similar to that employed for a rectangle.

The triangle *ABC* (Fig. 31) is regarded as composed of a large number of very narrow strips such as *DE*.

This strip, being very narrow, may be regarded as having its C.G. at the centre of the strip.

The centres of all such strips parallel to it will therefore lie on the straight line joining *A* to *R*, the centre of *BC*. This straight line *AR* is a median of the triangle.

Similarly the centres of all such strips parallel to *AC* lie on the median *BP*.

∴ the C.G. of the triangle lies at *G*, the intersection of the medians.

It follows that the third median, *CQ*, must pass through *G* and contains the C.G.s of all strips parallel to *AB*.

In Geometry it is proved that G is one of the points of trisection of each median.

$$\therefore \qquad \begin{aligned} BG &= 2PG \\ AG &= 2RG \\ CG &= 2QG. \end{aligned}$$

31. Centre of gravity of equal particles at the angles of a triangle.

It is useful to note that the C.G. of a triangular lamina is the same as that of three particles each of which has a weight which is one-third of that of the triangle, placed at the angular points of the triangle.

Let the weight of $\triangle ABC$ (Fig. 32) be W.

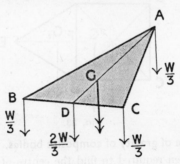

FIG. 32.

Let particles each of weight $\dfrac{W}{3}$ be placed at the angular points.

As we have seen (§ 25), particles of $\dfrac{W}{3}$ acting at B and C are equivalent to $\dfrac{2W}{3}$ acting at D, where D is the mid point of BC.

$\therefore$ the C.G. of the system must be same as that of $\dfrac{2W}{3}$ acting at D and $\dfrac{W}{3}$ acting at A.

But C.G. of $\frac{2W}{3}$ at D and $\frac{W}{3}$ at A is

$$\frac{2W}{3} + \frac{W}{3} \text{ at } G,$$

where AD is a median and

$$AG : GD = \frac{2W}{3} : \frac{W}{3} = 2 : 1.$$

Thus G must be the C.G. of the three particles. But it is also the C.G. of the $\triangle ABC$.

∴ the two C.G.'s coincide.

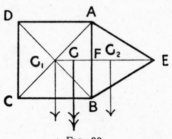

FIG. 33.

32. Centre of gravity of composite bodies.

It is often required to find the centre of gravity of a lamina composed of two or more regular figures. If the centre of gravity of each of these is known, the centre of gravity of the whole figure can be found by methods shown in the following examples :

Example I. *To find the centre of gravity of a uniform lamina consisting of a square and an equilateral triangle constructed on one side.*

In problems connected with lamina of uniform structure and thickness, the mass, and consequently the weight, of a lamina is proportional to its surface area.

∴ when taking moments the areas may be used as representing the actual weights.

In Fig. 33 G_1 the intersection of diagonals is the C.G. of the square.

Also EG_1 is an axis of geometrical symmetry for the whole figure.

∴ C.G. of the △ and of the composite figure will lie on this line.

But C.G. of △ is at G_2, where FG_2 is $\frac{1}{3}$ of the median EF.

If $\quad\quad\quad a = $ length of side of square,

∴ $\quad\quad\quad a^2 = $ area of square

also $\quad\quad\quad EF = a \times \dfrac{\sqrt{3}}{2}$ $\quad$ (*Trigonometry*, p. 80),

$$FG_2 = \frac{1}{3}a \times \frac{\sqrt{3}}{2} = \frac{a\sqrt{3}}{6}.$$

and $\quad \triangle AEB = \dfrac{1}{2}a \times \dfrac{a\sqrt{3}}{2} = \dfrac{a^2\sqrt{3}}{4}$

Taking the weight of each figure as concentrated at its C.G. we have:

(1) a^2 acting at G_1.

(2) $\dfrac{a^2\sqrt{3}}{4}$ acting at G_2.

∴ C.G. of the whole is at G, where

G_1G_2 is divided at G in the ratio $a^2 : \dfrac{a^2\sqrt{3}}{4}$.

$\quad\quad$ *i.e.,* $\quad$,, $\quad\quad$,, $\quad 4 : \sqrt{3}.$

Example 2. *To find the centre of gravity of a quadrilateral lamina.*

First method. The following method is useful for finding the C.G. by drawing.

(1) In the quadrilateral $ABCD$ (Fig. 34) draw the diagonal AC.

Consider △s ABC, ADC.

Let weights be W_1 and W_2.

Take E, the mid point of AC. Join DE, BE.

C.G. of ADC is at G_1, where $EG_1 = \frac{1}{3}ED$.

C.G. of ABC ,, G_2 ,, $EG_2 = \frac{1}{3}EB$.

Join G_1G_2.

Then C.G. of the whole quadrilateral is at G, where $G_1G : G_2G = W_1 : W_2$.

(2) Draw the diagonal BD (dotted line) and so divide the quadrilateral into $\triangle$s ABD, DBC.

Now proceed as before to join the C.G.s these $\triangle$s, viz., G_3 and G_4 (dotted lines used throughout).

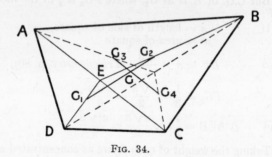

FIG. 34.

$\therefore$ C.G. of quadrilateral lies on G_3G_4, but it also lies on G_1G_2.

$\therefore$ it lies at G, their point of intersection.

Second method. This method is similar to that in §31 for a triangle.

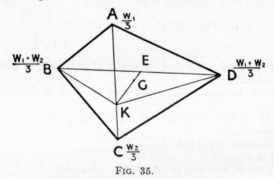

FIG. 35.

In Fig. 35, let weight of $\triangle ABD = W_1$.

,,   ,,   ,, $\triangle BCD = W_2$.

C.G. of $\triangle ABD$ is same as $\dfrac{W_1}{3}$ at points A, B, D.

C.G. of $\triangle BCD$ is same as $\dfrac{W_2}{3}$ at points B, C, D.

$\therefore$ C.G. of quadrilateral is the same as :

$$\dfrac{W_1}{3} \text{ at } A,$$

$$\dfrac{W_1}{3} + \dfrac{W_2}{3} \text{ at } B,$$

$$\dfrac{W_2}{3} \text{ at } C,$$

$$\dfrac{W_1}{3} + \dfrac{W_2}{3} \text{ at } D.$$

Let AC be divided at K in ratio $W_1 : W_2$—$i.e.$, wts. of $\triangle$s.

Then $\dfrac{W_1}{3}$ at A and $\dfrac{W_2}{3}$ at C are equivalent to $\dfrac{W_1}{3} + \dfrac{W_2}{3}$ acting at K.

Since we have $\dfrac{W_1 + W_2}{3}$ acting at points B, K, D

$\therefore$ C.G. of quadrilateral is the same as that of $\triangle BKD$.

$\therefore$ if E is mid point of BD

C.G. of quadrilateral is at G on EK, where $EG = \tfrac{1}{3}EK$.

33. Use of moments in finding centre of gravity.

One of the most valuable and effective methods of finding the centre of gravity is by an application of the principle of moments.

If a body or system of bodies is made up of a number of parts whose weights and centres of gravity are known, the sum of these parts is their resultant, and it acts at the centre of gravity of the whole.

Consequently the moment about any axis of the resultant acting at the centre of gravity of the whole is equal to the sum of the moments of the parts acting at their centres of gravity.

This can be expressed generally as follows :

Let $w_1, w_2, w_3 \ldots$ be a series of weights whose distances from a given axis are $d_1, d_2, d_3 \ldots$

The sum of their moments about this axis is

$$w_1d_1 + w_2d_2 + w_3d_3 + \ldots$$

Let $\bar{x}$ be distance of C.G. of the whole from the axis about which moments are taken.

Then moment of the resultant about the axis is

$$(w_1 + w_2 + w_3 + \ldots) \times \bar{x}.$$

But moment of resultant = moments of the parts.

$\therefore (w_1 + w_2 + w_3 + \ldots) \times \bar{x} = w_1d_1 + w_2d_2 + w_3d_3 + \ldots$

$$\therefore \quad \bar{x} = \frac{w_1d_1 + w_2d_2 + w_3d_3 + \ldots}{w_1 + w_2 + w_3 + \ldots}$$

i.e., dist. of C.G. from axis $= \dfrac{\text{sum of moments of parts}}{\text{sum of weights of parts}}$

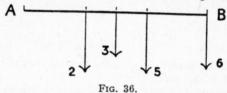

FIG. 36.

Similarly if any other axis were taken, and if $\bar{y}$ is the distance of the C.G. from that axis, $\bar{y}$ can be similarly determined.

34. Worked Examples.

Example 1. *A uniform rod AB is 6 ft. long and weighs 3 lbs. Weights are placed on it as follows : 2 lbs. at 2 ft. from A, 5 lbs. at 4 ft. from A, and 6 lbs. at B. How far is the centre of gravity of the whole system from A ?*

The arrangement of the forces is shown in Fig. 36.

Take moments about an axis at A. The sum of moments of the three weights and the weight of the rod acting at the centre of the rod must equal the moment of the resultant acting at the unknown centre of gravity of the whole.

Let $\bar{x}$ = distance of the C.G. from A.

Resultant   = sum of weights
              $= 2 + 5 + 6 + 3$
              $= 16.$

Equating moments about A:
$16 \times \bar{x} = (2 \times 2) + (5 \times 4) + (6 \times 6) + (3 \times 3)$
              $= 69$
$\therefore$ $\bar{x} = \frac{69}{16} = 4\frac{5}{16}$ ft. from A.

Example 2. *Find the centre of gravity of a thin uniform lamina as shown in Fig.* 37.

Let the weight of a sq. in. of the lamina be w lbs.

Wt. of $ABCD = (8 \times 2)w$
$= 16w$ lbs.

C.G. of $ABCD$ is at G_1, where G_1 is the intersection of the diagonals and $OG_1 = 1$ in., where O is the centre of AD.

Wt. of $EFKN = (8 \times 1\frac{1}{2})w$
$= 12w$ lbs.

C.G. of $EFKN$ is at G_2, where $OG_2 = 6$ in. and G_1G_2 is the symmetrical axis of the figure.

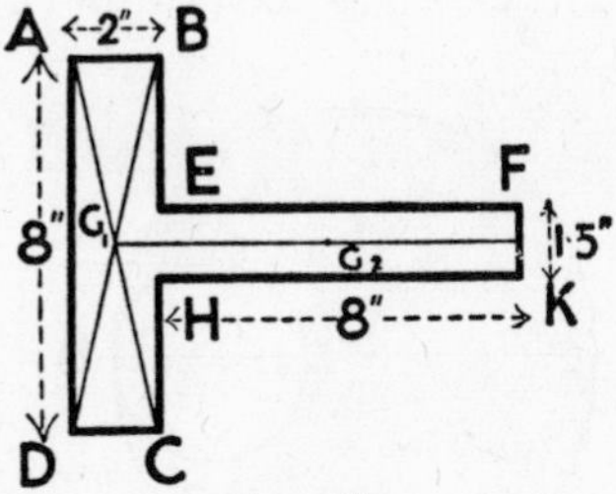

FIG. 37.

$\therefore$ Total weight $= 16w + 12w = 28w.$

This acts at an unknown C.G.

Let distance of C.G. from O be $\bar{x}$.

Taking moments about AD.
$$28w \times \bar{x} = (16w \times 1) + (12w \times 6)$$
$$= 88w$$
$$\therefore \qquad \bar{x} = \frac{88w}{28w} = \frac{22}{7} \text{ in.}$$

Example 3. *Find the centre of gravity of a thin uniform circular metal plate of radius* 12 *in., when there has been cut out a circular piece of metal of radius* 4 *in. which touches the circumference of the plate.*

Let AB (Fig. 38) be a diameter of circle.

Let CB be a diameter of circle cut out.

By symmetry C.G. of remainder lies on AB.

Let w lbs. $=$ weight of plate per sq. in.

Let G be position of the required centre of gravity.

Weight of whole circle $= (\pi \times 12^2 \times w)$ lbs.
,,   cut-out circle $= (\pi \times 4^2 \times w)$ lbs.
,,   remainder $= \pi(144 - 16)w$ lbs.
                                   $= 128\pi w$ lbs.

Now the moments of the weight of the whole circle about any axis must equal the sum of the moments of the circle cut and the remainder.

I.e., moment of whole circle at O = moment of remainder at G + moment of circle cut out acting at the centre.

∴ moment of remainder at G = moment of whole circle at O — moment of circle cut out.

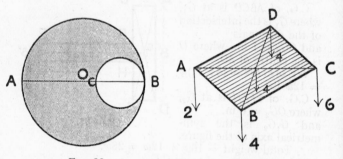

FIG. 38.   FIG. 39.

Taking moments about A.

$$128\pi w \times AG = 144\pi w \times 12 - 16\pi w \times 20.$$
$$\therefore \qquad 128AG = 144 \times 12 - 16 \times 20 = 1408.$$
$$\therefore \qquad AG = \frac{1408}{128} = 11 \text{ in.}$$

Example 4. *Weights of 2 lbs., 4 lbs., 6 lbs., 4 lbs. are placed at the corners A, B, C, D of a uniform square lamina of weight 4 lbs. The side of the square is 12 in. Find the distance of the centre of gravity of the whole from AB and AD.*

Fig. 39 represents the square and the arrangement of the weights.

The C.G. of the lamina itself is at O, the intersection of the diagonals.

(1) Take moments about AB.

Let $\bar{x}$ = distance of C.G. of the whole from AB.

The turning moments about the axis AB of weights at A and B, on the axis itself, will be zero.

Weight of the whole system $= 2 + 4 + 6 + 4 + 4 = 20$ lbs.

Now, moment of the resultant—*i.e.*, 20 lbs. acting at unknown C.G. = sum of moments of parts of the system.

$$\therefore\ 20 \times \bar{x} = (6 \times 12) + (4 \times 12) + (4 \times 6)$$
$$= 144$$
$$\therefore\qquad \bar{x} = \frac{144}{20} = 7\tfrac{1}{5} \text{ in.}$$

(2) Taking moments about AD.

Let $\bar{y}$ = distance of C.G. of whole from AD.

Then the equation of moments, found as before, is :
$$20 \times \bar{y} = (4 \times 6) + (6 \times 12) + (4 \times 12)$$
$$= 144$$
$$\therefore\qquad y = 7\tfrac{1}{5} \text{ in.}$$

$\therefore$ The centre of gravity is $7\tfrac{1}{5}$ in. from AB and AD.

Check: distance of C.G. from CB and CD could be similarly calculated.

Exercise 4.

1. On a light rod AB, 6 ft. long, weights of 3 lbs. and 5 lbs. are hung at distances of 2 ft. and 5 ft. from A. Where will the centre of gravity be?

2. If the rod in the last question were uniform and weighed 2 lbs., where would the centre of gravity of the whole be?

3. On a light rod AB, 5 ft. long, weights of 2 lbs., 4 lbs., 6 lbs., and 8 lbs. are hung at intervals of 1 ft. between A and B. Find the centre of gravity of the whole.

4. On a light rod AB, 5 ft. long, weights of 2 lbs., 6 lbs., and 4 lbs. are placed at distances of $\tfrac{1}{2}$ ft., 1 ft., and $2\tfrac{1}{2}$ ft., respectively, from A. What weight must be placed 4 ft. from A if the centre of gravity is to be 2·45 ft. from A?

5. ABC is an isosceles triangle without weight. $AC = AB = 6$ ft., and $BC = 4$ ft. Weights of 1 lb., 2 lbs.,

2 lbs., are hung at A, B, and C, respectively. How far is the centre of gravity of these from BC?

6. ABC is a triangle whose weight is 2 lbs. Weights of 2 lbs., 4 lbs., and 4 lbs. are placed at A, B, and C, respectively. What is the position of the centre of gravity of the whole?

7. Find the centre of gravity of a uniform piece of cardboard consisting of a square $ABCD$ of side 6 in. and an isosceles triangle BCE constructed on a side BC of the square and having an altitude FE, 4 in. long.

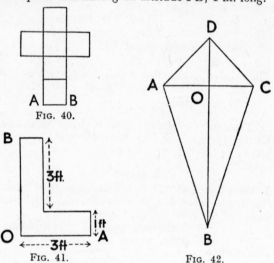

FIG. 40.

FIG. 41.

FIG. 42.

8. Fig. 40 represents a cross containing six squares, each a square inch. It is made of thin uniform metal. Find the centre of gravity of the cross from AB.

9. Find the centre of gravity of a uniform lamina of the shape and dimensions shown in Fig. 41, giving its distance from OA and OB.

10. The lamina shown in Fig. 42 consists of two isosceles triangles ABC, ADC. The diagonals AC and BD are 6 in. and 8 in., respectively, and OD is 2 in. Find the distance of the centre of gravity of the whole from B.

11. Find the centre of gravity of six thin uniform metal discs, arranged as shown in Fig. 43. The diameter of each circle is 1 in.

12. Weights of 2 lbs., 3 lbs., 4 lbs., 5 lbs. are placed at the corners *A*, *B*, *C*, *D*, respectively, of a square of side 10 in. and weighing 2 lbs. Find the position of the centre of gravity from *AB* and *AD*.

35. Centre of gravity of regular solids.

The centres of gravity of a few regular solids are given below, in most cases without proof, as these require more advanced mathematics to be satisfactory.

Symmetrical solids. The centres of gravity of those solids which are symmetrical bodies, such as cylinders,

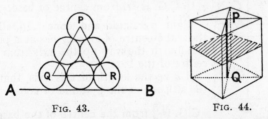

Fig. 43.   Fig. 44.

spheres, etc., are at the geometrically symmetrical centres, since the mass of a symmetrical solid will balance about that point.

Rectangular prism.

This is a symmetrical body, but a proof, similar to that employed for a lamina, is given, because of the general usefulness of the method.

Fig. 44 shows a rectangular right prism in which is indicated a very thin lamina, cut at right angles to the axis of the prism, and therefore parallel to the two bases. This lamina is a rectangle in shape, and its centre of gravity is at the centre of it—that is, at the intersection of the diagonals. It will therefore lie on the axis of the prism, which is the straight line joining the inter-sections of the diameters of the bases. If the prism is conceived as being made up of a large number of such laminæ, the centre of gravity of them all will lie on the axis. From the symmetry of the solid the centre of gravity will therefore be at the middle point of the axis.

The cylinder is a special case of the prism, a section, at right angles to the axis, always being a circle. The centre of gravity is therefore at the centre of the axis.

Sphere. The centre of gravity of a sphere is obviously at the centre.

Hemisphere. The centre of gravity of a hemisphere requires more advanced mathematics for its determination than is assumed in this book. It lies on the radius drawn perpendicular to the base from the centre and is three-eighths of the length of the radius from the base.

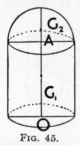

FIG. 45.

If r be the radius, the

C.G. is $\frac{3}{8}r$. from centre of base.

Right pyramids and cone. In all of these the centre of gravity lies at a point one-fourth the way up the axis from the centre of the base.

If h be the length of this axis, that is, the altitude of the pyramid or cone,

C.G. is $\frac{h}{4}$ from the centre of the base.

36. Worked example. *A cylinder of height 10 in. and radius of base 4 in. is surmounted by a hemisphere of the same radius as that of the base of the cylinder, and made of the same material. Find the distance of the centre of gravity the composite body from the centre of the base of the cylinder.*

In Fig. 45 G_1, the mid point of OA, the axis of the cylinder is the C.G. of that body. G_2 is the C.G. of the hemisphere and $AG_2 = \frac{3}{8}r$, where r is the radius.

Vol. of cylinder $= \pi r^2 h$ ($h =$ the height)
$$= \pi \times 4^2 \times 10 = 160\pi \text{ c. in.}$$

Vol. of hemisphere $= \frac{2}{3}\pi r^3$
$$= \frac{2}{3}\pi \times 64 = \frac{128\pi}{3} \text{ c. in.}$$

$\therefore$ Total vol. $= 160\pi + \frac{128\pi}{3} = \frac{608\pi}{3} \text{ c. in.}$

Also $\qquad OG_1 = \dfrac{h}{2} = 5$ in.

$$OG_2 = 10 + (\tfrac{3}{8} \times 4) = \tfrac{23}{2} \text{ in.}$$

Let $\bar{y} =$ distance of C.G. of whole from O.

Since the bodies are of the same material, the weights are proportional to their volumes.

Taking moments about O.

$$\frac{608\pi}{3} \times \bar{y} = (160\pi \times 5) + \left(\frac{128\pi}{3} \times \frac{23}{2}\right)$$

$$\therefore \qquad \bar{y} \times \frac{608}{3} = 800 + \frac{1472}{3} = \frac{3872}{3}$$

$$\therefore \qquad \bar{y} = \frac{3872}{3} \times \frac{3}{608}$$

$$= 6.37 \text{ in. approximately.}$$

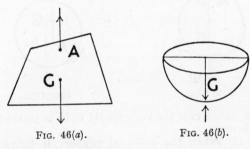

FIG. 46(a).   FIG. 46(b).

37. Equilibrium of bodies.

We have seen (§ 28) that a body which is suspended from a point on or near a boundary will be in equilibrium when the point of suspension and the centre of gravity are in the same vertical line (Fig. 46(a)). Similarly if a body is resting on a surface (Fig. 46(b)), the centre of gravity and the point of support are in the same straight line. In each case the body is acted upon by :

(1) Its weight acting vertically downwards at the centre of gravity.

(2) An equal and opposite force acting vertically

upward at the point of suspension or point of support.

38. Stable, unstable, and neutral equilibrium.

Suppose that a body which is suspended in equilibrium receives a slight displacement (Fig. 47(b)). Three cases must be considered :

(1) **When the point of suspension is above the C.G.** Then the weight acting at the centre of gravity G, Fig. 47(a), being no longer in a vertical line with the force T at the point of suspension, A, exerts a turning moment, $W \times AB$, which tends to swing the body back to its original position.

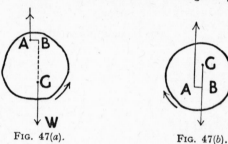

FIG. 47(a).　　　FIG. 47(b).

In such a case the body is said to be in stable equilibrium.

(2) **When the point of support is below the centre of gravity.** In this case, as will be seen from Fig. 47(b), the weight acting at G exerts a turning moment which tends to turn the body away from its original position. The body is then said to be in unstable equilibrium.

(3) **When the point of suspension is at the centre of gravity**, as, for example, of a circular lamina at its centre, or a wheel at its axis. Any displacement of the body in its own vertical plane will result in it remaining at rest in its new position.

Such a body is said to be in neutral equilibrium.

If the body is resting on a horizontal surface, such

as a billiard ball on a table (Fig. 48), the forces acting are the weight of the ball downwards and the thrust (R) of the table upwards. If there is a displacement, the ball will tend to come to rest with its centre of gravity, G, vertically over a new point of support.

39. Definitions of equilibrium and examples.

(1) Stable equilibrium.

A body is said to be in stable equilibrium when, on receiving a slight displacement, it tends to return to its original position.

Any body with a relatively large base, resting on a horizontal support and with a comparatively low centre of gravity, is stable. The following are a few examples : a right prism or a cylinder resting on a base ; a cone resting on its base ; this book resting on its side.

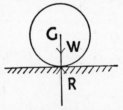

A necessary condition of stability is that the centre of gravity is vertically above what may be described as the contour of its base. In the case of a body

FIG. 48.

with more than one support, this includes not only the area of the ground covered by each support but also the area between them. For example, a table with four legs is stable because of the large area included between the legs and the straight lines joining them. This is important in many of the actions of life which depend on accurate balancing. In the case of a man standing up, the contour of his base is not only the actual area of the surface covered by his feet, but also that area between them and straight lines drawn from toe to toe and heel to heel. So long as the man's centre of gravity is vertically over this area he maintains his balance easily. That is why in cases where there is lateral swaying, as in a bus, a train, or a ship, a man instinctively places his feet farther apart, and so increases his base contour.

The student may easily work out for himself problems of balancing connected with riding a bicycle, walking on a narrow ledge, etc.

(2) Unstable equilibrium.

A body is said to be in unstable equilibrium when, on receiving a slight displacement, it tends to go farther away from its position of rest.

A body with a small base and a high C.G. is usually unstable. Examples are : a cone resting on its vertex from which a small piece has been cut off, a lead pencil balanced on its base, a narrow book standing upright on a table, etc.

(3) Neutral equilibrium.

A body is in neutral equilibrium when, on receiving a slight displacement, it tends to come to rest in its new position.

Examples are a ball, a cylinder lying on its curved surface, a hemisphere lying on its curved surface, a cone lying on its oblique surface, etc.

Exercise 5.

1. A cone of altitude 6 in. is placed on top of a cylinder whose base is the same area as the base of the cone, and whose height is 6 in. The axes of the bodies are in the same straight line. How far is the centre of gravity of the composite figure from the base of the cylinder? Both bodies are of the same material.

2. A cone of height 4 in. and radius of base 2 in. is fastened to the flat surface of a hemisphere whose base has the same area as the base of the cone. If the two bodies are made of the same material, find the centre of gravity of the composite body.

3. A uniform piece of wire is bent to the shape of an isosceles triangle with a base of 16 in. and each of the equal sides 10 in. Find the centre of gravity of the triangular wire.

4. From a uniform circular disc of diameter 12 in. and mass 4 lbs., a circular piece, 3 in. in diameter, is removed, the shortest distance between the circum-

ferences of the circles being 1 in. Find the position of the centre of gravity of the remainder.

Hint.—Remember that the masses of the circular discs are proportional to the squares of their diameters.

5. From a rectangular lamina 10 in. by 8 in. a square of 4 in. side is cut out of one corner. Find the distance of the centre of gravity of the remainder from the uncut sides.

6. From one of the corners of an equilateral triangle of 4 in. side an equilateral triangle of 2 in. side is removed. Determine the position of the centre of gravity of the remaining figure.

7. State in the following cases whether the equilibrium is stable, unstable, or neutral :—

(1) A door which swings about hinges with a vertical axis.

(2) A book lying on its side on a table, with its centre of gravity just vertically over the edge of the table.

(3) A spherical marble lying in a basin with a spherical-shaped bottom.

(4) A ladder 30 ft. long resting against a vertical wall, with its foot on the ground and 4 in. from the wall.

CHAPTER IV

RESULTANT OF NON-PARALLEL FORCES
THE PARALLELOGRAM OF FORCE

40. Geometric representation of a force.

When investigating theorems and problems connected with forces we find it convenient to represent a force completely by a straight line.

For this purpose the straight line must show:

(1) The **direction** of its line of action, in relation to some fixed direction.

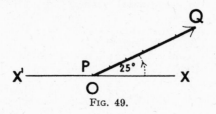

FIG. 49.

(2) The **sense** in which it acts along the line of action.

(3) The **magnitude**, shown by the length of the line, measured on a suitable scale.

Thus in Fig. 49, PQ represents a force of 6 units acting at a point O, making an angle of 25° with the direction of $X'OX$. The **sense** in which it acts along PQ is from P to Q; this is indicated by the arrow-head, and also by the order of the letters when describing it as the force PQ. If it acted from Q to P we should describe it as the force QP, and the arrow-head would be reversed.

41. Vector quantity. A quantity such as a force, which possesses both **direction and magnitude** is called a **vector quantity**, and the straight line by which it is represented, as *PQ* above, is called a **vector**.

Other examples of vector quantities with which we shall be concerned in later chapters are displacements, velocities, and accelerations.

Vectors are employed in the graphical solution of many problems, and the student would do well to acquire some elementary knowledge of them. This can be found in books on Practical Mathematics, such as *National Certificate Mathematics*, which is published by the English Universities Press.

42. Non-parallel forces acting on a body.

The forces with which we were concerned in the previous chapters have been parallel and acting in the same direction. We have seen how a number of such forces acting on a body can be replaced by a single force called the **resultant**, whose magnitude is equal to the algebraic sum of the magnitudes of the separate forces.

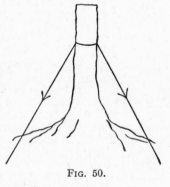

We now proceed to consider forces which are not parallel but concurrent; we must ascertain if such forces can have a resultant and how it may be obtained.

FIG. 50.

A practical example of the problem involved may help in understanding our object.

Suppose that two men were pulling down a tree by means of ropes attached to it at the same height. If they were to pull on ropes which were parallel, or if they pulled in the same direction on the one rope, the total force exerted would be the sum of the separate pulls. But in that case the direction of the fall of the tree might bring it on top of them.

If, however, they were to pull in different directions, as suggested in Fig. 50, they know from experience that the tree would fall somewhere between the lines of action of the forces exerted by them.

Clearly this could have been accomplished by a single force which would have the same effect as the two forces, though not equal to their sum, and acting somewhere between. This force would be the **resultant** of the two forces.

Thus we want to discover how to obtain both the magnitude and direction of the resultant of two such forces, acting in different directions on a body.

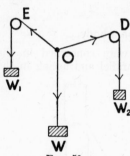

FIG. 51.

43. Resultant of two forces acting at a point.

The method by which the resultant can be obtained is best demonstrated, at this stage, by experiments. The principle to be adopted will be the same as that which was used for obtaining the resultant of parallel forces. We will find what force will produce equilibrium when two forces are acting at a point. This must be equal and opposite to the resultant which can replace the two forces.

Experiment. The actual apparatus employed is shown in Fig. 51. Three cords are knotted together at a point. Two of them are passed over smooth pulleys and attached to different weights. A sufficient weight is attached to the third string to keep the others in equilibrium.

We have seen that if a string passes over a smooth pulley the direction only of the tension in the string is altered, not the magnitude of it. If the suspended weights are W_1 and W_2, then forces equal to these act along the strings. Since there is equilibrium, the tension in these strings must be balanced by the weight, called W, hung on the third string.

Since W is equal and opposite to the combined effects of W_1 and W_2, it must be equal and opposite to their resultant, and its line of action is that of the third string.

We now draw on the surface of the board, or on paper placed on it, straight lines corresponding to the strings OF, OD, OE, shown in Fig. 52.

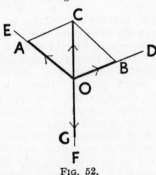

FIG. 52.

Choosing a suitable scale :

Along OD mark off OB to represent the force acting along OD—i.e., W_2.

Along OE mark off OA to represent the force acting along OE—i.e., W_1.

Along OF mark off OG to represent the third force W, acting along OF.

Draw AC parallel to OB and BC parallel to OA.

Then $OACB$ is a parallelogram.

1. If FO is produced it will be found to pass through C, so that OC is a diagonal of the parallelogram.

2. Now measure OC. It will be found to be equal to OG.

∴ on the scale in which OA represents W_2 and OB represents W_1, OC must represent W in magnitude.

But W is the force which is in equilibrium with W_1 and W_2.

∴ just as the force W represented by OG, acting downwards, maintains equilibrium, the force represented by OC, acting in the opposite direction, must be the resultant of W_1 and W_2.

∴ the diagonal of the parallelogram $OACB$ represents in magnitude and direction the resultant of the forces represented by OA and OB.

This experiment should be repeated with different values for W_1 and W_2, and consequently different values of W.

In every case, making allowances for slight errors, you will come to the same conclusion—viz., that—

If two forces, represented by OA and OB, act at a point O, and include between them the angle AOB, then if the parallelogram $OACB$ be completed, the diagonal of this parallelogram which passes through O represents in magnitude and direction the resultant of the forces. This is the theorem known as the Parallelogram of Forces. It may be defined thus :

Parallelogram of Forces.—*If two forces acting at a point are represented in magnitude and direction by two adjacent sides of a parallelogram, the diagonal of the parallelogram which passes through the point will represent their resultant in magnitude and direction.*

44. Forces acting at a point.

The definition of parallelogram of forces refers to two forces acting at a point; at times we speak of forces acting " on a body ". In a strict sense a force cannot act " at a point " if a " point " is used with a geometrical meaning. What is implied is that the lines of action of the forces meet at a point—that is, they are concurrent. This is a necessary hypothesis of the theorem. The forces act on a body, but the point of intersection of their lines of action does not necessarily lie in the body itself.

If, for example, we consider the case of two ropes attached to a tree (§ 42), and by means of which forces act on the tree, the ropes themselves will not meet, but the lines of action of the forces exerted by means of them must meet if the parallelogram of forces is to apply to them.

In Fig. 53, which shows a section of the tree, A and B represent the points on the body of the tree at which the forces P and Q are applied, and the lines AP and BQ show the directions of the forces. These, when produced, meet at a point O, which may or may not lie within the tree.

Nevertheless if we desire to construct a parallelogram for the forces P and Q, so that their resultant may be found, the point at which the sides of the parallelogram, which represent the forces meet, would represent the point O.

A force may be considered as acting at any point on its line of action. Consequently the force P may be considered as acting anywhere along OA. Similarly, Q may be considered as acting at any point on OB. Hence the two forces may be considered as acting at O.

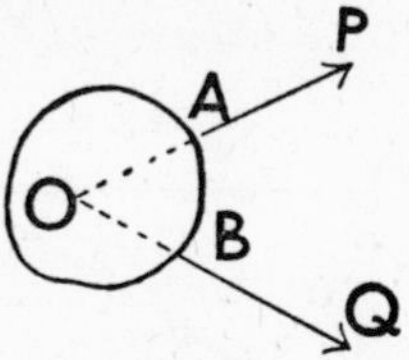

45. To calculate the resultant of two forces.

The problem of calculating the magnitude and direction of the

Fig. 53.

resultant by means of the parallelogram of force may be solved either by drawing or by calculation :

(1) The **drawing method** needs no explanation. This method must be used by students who have an insufficient knowledge of trigonometry. It is a useful, and sometimes an essential method, and with great care a fair degree of accuracy may be reached.

(2) The **method of calculation**. For this a working knowledge of trigonometry is essential. The student who is weak in the subject can consult the companion book to this volume, *Teach Yourself Trigonometry*, and when necessary, in the work which follows, references will be given to the appropriate pages in that book.

We will proceed to develop the method of calculation. Two cases may occur.

A. When the angle between the forces is a right angle—that is, the parallelogram is a rectangle.

In Fig. 54, OA, OB represent in magnitude and direction the forces P and Q. The rectangle $OACB$ is completed. Then the diagonal through O—i.e., OC—represents the resultant, R, of the two forces.

Let α be the angle between the force Q and the resultant. Then $90° - \alpha$ is the angle between R and P.

We require to find R and α.

(For methods employed see *Trigonometry*, § 61.)

(1) To find R:

OBC being a right-angled triangle

$$OC = \sqrt{OB^2 + BC^2}.$$
$$\therefore \qquad R = \sqrt{P^2 + Q^2}.$$

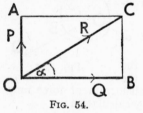

FIG. 54.

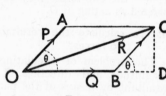

FIG. 55.

(2) To find α:

$$\tan \alpha = \frac{CB}{OB} = \frac{P}{Q}.$$

whence α is determined.

To find forces P and Q when R and α are known.

From $\triangle OBC$

$$P = R \sin \alpha.$$
$$Q = R \cos \alpha$$

B. When the angle between the forces is not a right angle.

In Fig. 55, OA, OB represent forces P and Q, and θ is the angle between them.

The parallelogram $OACB$ is constructed.

Then R represents the resultant of P and Q.

Produce OB to meet perpendicular from C at D.
Since OA and BC are parallel, $\angle CBD = \theta$.
Also $BC = OA$.
$\therefore$ BC represents P.

(1) To find R:

The sides OB and BC of $\triangle OBC$ are known, since they represent the magnitudes of the forces P and Q.

The connection between the sides of the triangle and the angle OBC is given by the formula

$$OC^2 = OB^2 + BC^2 - 2OB \cdot BC \cos OBC$$
$$(Trigonometry, \S 91).$$

But $\qquad \angle OBC = 180° - \theta.$
$\therefore \qquad \cos OBC = -\cos \theta$
$$(Trigonometry, \S 70).$$

Substituting
$$OC^2 = OB^2 + BC^2 - 2OB \cdot BC(-\cos \theta)$$
$$= OB^2 + BC^2 + 2OB \cdot BC \cos \theta.$$

$\therefore$ on substitution
$$R^2 = P^2 + Q^2 + 2PQ \cos \theta \quad . \quad . \quad (1)$$

From this R can be found when P, Q, and θ are known.

By a slight modification of the figure and proof, the same result may be obtained when $\angle AOB$ is greater than a right angle.

(2) To find α, the angle between Q and R:

From Fig. 55 we see
$$BD = BC \cos \theta$$
$$= P \cos \theta.$$
Similarly $\qquad CD = P \sin \theta.$
Now $\qquad \tan \alpha = \dfrac{CD}{OD} = \dfrac{CD}{OB + BD}.$

Substituting values found above
$$\tan \alpha = \frac{P \sin \theta}{Q + P \cos \theta} \quad . \quad . \quad (2)$$

From this formula α may be calculated.
Also $\qquad \angle AOC = \theta - \alpha.$

(3) **To find θ when P, Q, and R are known:**

These may be found by transforming formula **(1)** above, viz.:

$$R^2 = P^2 + Q^2 + 2PQ \cos \theta.$$

From this

$$\cos \theta = \frac{R^2 - P^2 - Q^2}{2PQ} \quad . \quad . \quad . \quad (3)$$

(4) **To find R when P and Q are equal:**

The parallelogram which was described in Fig. 55 now becomes a rhombus : therefore,

(a) $\angle \theta$ is bisected and R makes an angle $\frac{\theta}{2}$ with both P and Q.

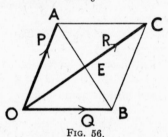

FIG. 56.

(b) The diagonals bisect each other at right angles.

$\therefore \triangle$s OEA, OEB are right-angled.

$$\therefore \quad \frac{OE}{OB} = \cos EOB$$

$$= \cos \frac{\theta}{2}.$$

$$\therefore \quad OE = OB \cos \frac{\theta}{2}.$$

But $OC = 2 \times OE$.

$$\therefore \quad OC = 2OB \,.\, \cos \frac{\theta}{2} \text{ on substitution for } OE.$$

or $R = 2Q \cos \dfrac{\theta}{2} \,.$ . . . . . . (4)

46. Summary of formulae.

The above formulæ are used so frequently in solving the problems, that they are collected for future reference.

(1) To find R:
$$R^2 = P^2 + Q^2 + 2P \cdot Q \cdot \cos \theta.$$

(2) To find α:
$$\tan \alpha = \frac{P \sin \theta}{Q + P \cos \theta}.$$

(3) To find θ:
$$\cos \theta = \frac{R^2 - P^2 - Q^2}{2PQ}.$$

(4) To find R when P and Q are equal:
$$R = 2Q \cos \frac{\theta}{2}.$$

47. Resultant of a number of forces acting at a point.

When more than two forces act at a point the resultant of them all can be found by repeated application of the parallelogram law for two forces. We proceed as follows :

The resultant of two forces is found. Let it be R_1.

Next the resultant of R_1 and a third force is found. Let it be R_2.

Similarly the resultant of R_2 and a fourth force is found. This process is repeated until the resultant of all the forces has been found.

In practice this method is often long and tedious, but by careful drawing a practical solution can be obtained.

An alternative method will be given later.

48. Worked Examples.

Example I.—*Forces of 7 lbs. wt. and 5 lbs. wt. act on a body, and the angle between them is 55°. Find their resultant and the angles between it and the two forces.*

Fig. 57 represents the given forces

Required to find R and α.

(1) To find R:

Using formula (1)

$$R^2 = P^2 + Q^2 + 2PQ \cos \theta,$$

and substituting the given values of P, Q and θ.

$$R^2 = 5^2 + 7^2 + 2 \cdot 5 \cdot 7 \cos 55°$$
$$= 74 + 70 \times 0\cdot5736$$
$$= 114\cdot15.$$

$$\therefore \quad R = \sqrt{114\cdot15}$$
$$= 10\cdot7 \text{ lbs. approx.}$$

(2) To find α:

Using formula (2)

$$\tan \alpha = \frac{P \sin \theta}{Q + P \cos \theta}.$$

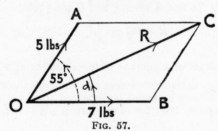

FIG. 57.

We have on substitution :

$$\tan \alpha = \frac{5 \sin 55°}{7 + 5 \cos 55°}$$
$$= \frac{5 \times 0\cdot8192}{7 + 5 \times 0\cdot5736}$$
$$= \frac{4\cdot0960}{9\cdot8680}.$$

$$\therefore \quad \log. \tan \alpha = \log 4\cdot0960 - \log 9\cdot8680$$
$$= 0\cdot6123 - 0\cdot9943$$
$$= \bar{1}\cdot6180$$
$$= \log \tan 22° 32'.$$

$$\therefore \quad \alpha = 22° 32'.$$

Also $\quad \angle AOC = \angle AOB - \alpha$
$$= 55° - 22° 32'$$
$$= 32° 28'.$$

This could be checked by calculating $\angle AOC$ separately, using formula (2).

Example 2.—*Two forces, P and Q, of 10 lbs. wt. and 14 lbs. wt., respectively, have a resultant of 22 lbs. wt. What is the angle between P and Q?*

If θ be the angle between P and Q,

Using, formula (3)

$$\cos \theta = \frac{R^2 - P^2 - Q^2}{2PQ}.$$

Substituting given values

$$\cos \theta = \frac{22^2 - 10^2 - 14^2}{2 \cdot 10 \cdot 14}$$

$$= \frac{188}{280} = 0.6714.$$

$$\therefore \qquad \theta = 47° 50'.$$

49. Moments of intersecting forces.

We have seen (§ 33) that the moments of a number of parallel forces about a point in their plane is equal to the moment of their resultant about the point.

We shall show that this is also true for intersecting

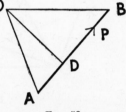

FIG. 58.

forces. First we will consider a graphic method of representing moments.

Graphical representation of moments.

Let AB, Fig. 58, represent a force P in magnitude and direction.

Let O be any point.

Join OA, OB.

Draw OD perpendicular to AB.

Since AB represents the force P, the turning moment of P about O is equal to the magnitude of the force multiplied by its distance from O,

i.e.,   moment of $P = AB \times OD$.

But area of $\triangle OAB = \frac{1}{2}(AB \times OD)$.

$\therefore$ **Area of $\triangle OAB = \frac{1}{2} \times$ (moment of P about O).**

This method will be employed in the following demonstration.

50. **The algebraic sum of the moments of two intersecting forces about a point in their plane is equal to the moment of their resultant about the same point.**

Let OA and OB (Fig. 59) represent in direction two forces P and Q intersecting at O.

Let X be any point in their plane.

Draw XAC parallel to OB and meeting the line of force P in A.

Let the scale with which the magnitudes of the forces P and Q are drawn be such that OA represents P and OB represents Q.

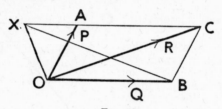

Fig. 59.

Draw BC parallel to OA to meet XAC in C.

Then $OACB$ is a parallelogram and OC, its diagonal, represents R, the resultant of P and Q.

Taking moments about X.

Moment of P is represented by $2 \times$ area of $\triangle OAX$.
     ,, Q ,,   ,, $2 \times$ area of $\triangle OBX$.
     ,, R ,,   ,, $2 \times$ area of $\triangle OCX$.

But $\triangle OCX = \triangle OAX + \triangle OAC$
and $\triangle OAC = \triangle OBC$
               $= \triangle OBX$ ($\triangle$s on same base and between same parallels).

$\therefore$ $\triangle OCX = \triangle OAX + \triangle OBX$
and $2 \times \triangle OCX = 2 \times \triangle OAX + 2 \times \triangle OBX$.

i.e., moment of R about X = moment of P about X.
                                       + moment of Q about X.

Note.—If the point X be taken on the line of action of R the moment of R vanishes.

Consequently the sum of the moments of P and Q about the same point also vanishes.

51. Worked Example.

Forces of 4 lbs. wt., 6 lbs. wt., and 8 lbs. wt. act along the sides of an equilateral triangle of 10 in. side, in directions shown in Fig. 60. Find the line of action of their resultant.

Let the line of action of resultant cut BC in X.

Draw XD and XE perpendicular to AB and AC.

Since X lies on the line of action of the resultant moments of the forces about X must vanish (§ 50, note).

Also as X lies on BC, the moment of the force along BC also vanishes.

∴ the sum of the moments of the forces along BA and CA must vanish.

∴ moment of force along BA = moment of force along CA.

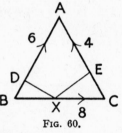

FIG. 60.

∴ $6 \times DX = 4 \times EX.$

But $DX = BX \sin 60$

and $EX = CX \sin 60.$

∴ $6 \times BX \sin 60 = 4 \times CX \sin 60.$

∴ $6BX = 4CX.$

∴ $\dfrac{BX}{CX} = \dfrac{4}{6}.$

∴ X must divide BC in the ratio $4 : 6$.

Similarly if a point Y be taken where the line of action of the resultant cuts AC, it will be found by the same reasoning that Y divides AC in the ratio $8 : 6$.

∴ the straight line joining the points X and Y will be the line of action of the resultant.

Exercise 6.

1. P and Q are two forces and R is their resultant. The angle between the forces is θ and angle between R and Q is α.

(a) Find R, when $P = 10$, $Q = 24$, $\theta = 90°$.
(b) Find R and α when $P = 16.5$, $Q = 22$, $\theta = 90°$.
(c) Find R when $P = 5$, $Q = 8$, $\theta = 42°$.
(d) Find R and α when $P = 4$, $Q = 6$, $\theta = 60$.
(e) Find θ when $P = 36$, $Q = 60$, $R = 80$.
(f) Find θ and α, when $P = 20$, $Q = 16$, $R = 28$.

2. In Fig. 61 is shown a weight of 5 lbs. suspended by a string from B which is drawn aside by a force acting along another string OA, knotted at O and stretched horizontally. It is thus held in equilibrium, the force acting along OA being 3 lbs. wt. Find :

(1) The pressure exerted at B.
(2) The angle which OB makes with the vertical.

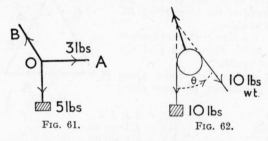

FIG. 61.   FIG. 62.

3. The resultant of two forces is 16 lbs. wt. One of the forces is 14 lbs. wt., and it makes an angle of 45° with the resultant. Find the other force.

[*Hint.*—Adapt formula (1) (see *Trigonometry*, § 103) or find the result by drawing.]

4. In Fig. 62 is shown the diagram of a weight of 10 lbs. sustained by a rope passing over a smooth pulley : the two parts of the rope include an angle of θ. Find the magnitude and direction of the resultant pressure on the pulley for the following values of θ :

(1) 0°; (2) 30°; (3) 45°; (4) 50°; (5) 60°; (6) 90°.

Plot your results on squared paper.

5. Two forces of 8 lbs. wt. and 7 lbs. wt. have a resultant

of 13 lbs. wt. What is the angle between the two forces?

6. Two forces of 14 lbs. wt. and 10 lbs. wt. have a resultant of 12·5 lbs. wt. Find the angle between them.

7. A wire suspended from two points A and B (see Fig. 63) supports at its centre a small smooth pulley,

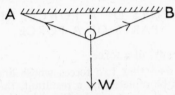

FIG. 63.

from which hangs a weight of W lbs. The angle between the two parts of the wire is 140° and the force exerted in each part of the wire is 150 lbs. wt. What is the amount of the load, W?

8. Two forces of 10 lbs. wt. and a force of 5 lbs. wt. act at a point, and the angle between each pair is 60°, as shown in Fig. 64.

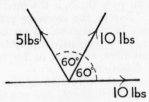

FIG. 64.

Find the resultant of the three forces.

9. Forces act along the sides of an equilateral triangle ABC as follows :

9 lbs. wt. from B to C.
6 lbs. wt. from C to A.
3 lbs. wt. from B to A.

In what ratio are the sides BC and CA cut by the resultant?

CHAPTER V

COMPONENTS OF A FORCE, RESOLVED PARTS OF A FORCE

52. Components of a force.

We have seen that two forces whose lines of action intersect can be replaced by a resultant, the magnitude and direction of which can be found by the application of the theorem " The Parallelogram of Forces ".

The two forces are called the **components** of the resultant force. The problem now to be considered is how these components are to be found when the resultant is known.

When applying the theorem of the " Parallelogram of Forces " to find the resultant of two known forces, there is only one solution, since but one diagonal of the parallelogram can pass through the intersection of two adjacent sides. But in the converse problem a given straight line may be a diagonal of an infinite number of parallelograms; consequently it may be the resultant of an infinite number of pairs of forces, differing in magnitude and direction.

When, however, the direction of one of the components is known, there is only one solution. In these circumstances the components may be found readily, either by drawing or by using the appropriate formula of the preceding chapter.

53. Resolving a force.

The case when the two unknown components are at right angles is much the most important from a practical point of view. The components thus obtained are called the resolved parts in the given direction and the process of obtaining them is called " resolving the force ".

Thus in Fig. 65 the force R, acting along and represented by OC, can be resolved into two forces, P and Q, one of which makes an angle θ with R, and the other which makes an angle of $90° - θ$ with R.

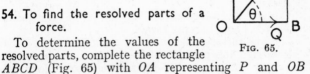

P and Q are the resolved parts of R in the direction θ and $90°—θ$ with R.

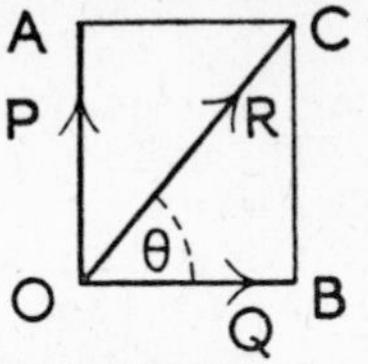

54. To find the resolved parts of a force.

To determine the values of the resolved parts, complete the rectangle

FIG. 65.

$ABCD$ (Fig. 65) with OA representing P and OB representing G.

Then $$\frac{OB}{OC} = \cos θ.$$

∴ $$OB = OC \cos θ.$$

But OB represents Q in magnitude and direction,
and OC ,, R ,, ,,

∴ $$Q = R \cos θ.$$

Also since $$BC = OA,$$

and $$\frac{BC}{OC} = \sin θ.$$

∴ $$OA = OC \sin θ,$$

i.e., $$P = R \sin θ.$$

∴ Resolved part of R along $OB = R \cos θ.$

and ,, ,, R ,, $OA = R \sin θ.$

Since a force has no effect in a direction at right angles to its own direction

$R \cos θ$ is the total effect of R in the direction OB, and $R \sin θ$ is the total effect of R in the direction OA.

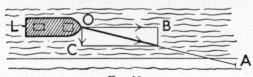

FIG. 66.

55. Illustrative example.

The following example will serve as a practical illustration of this principle. Fig. 66 represents a barge

LO, to which is attached at *O* a rope by means of which a horse at *A*, moving along the tow-path of a canal, drags the barge through the water. The pull of the horse, from the necessities of the case, cannot be a direct one, and consequently a certain amount of the effort is lost.

The useful part of the pull is in the direction indicated by *OB*.

This is the resolved part of the pull in the direction in which the barge is being towed.

Let θ be the angle between *OA* and *OB*.

Resolving the pull (*P*) of the horse in the direction shown by *OB* and also at right angles to it, along *OC*, we see, as shown in § 54, that *P* is resolved into

$$P \cos θ \text{ acting along } OB,$$
$$P \sin θ \text{ acting along } OC.$$

Thus the effective pull of the horse is $P \cos θ$, and $P \sin θ$ represents the lateral pull towards the bank which is neutralised by the set of the rudder.

The useful part of the pull of the horse thus depends on $\cos θ$. Now we know from Trigonometry that $\cos θ$ is always less than unity; consequently $P \cos θ$ is always less than *P*. Further, as an angle increases, the cosine decreases. Therefore as the pull is more effective when $\cos θ$ is large, θ should be as small as possible.

It is therefore advantageous, in general, that the rope should be long, because then θ is small. If it be too long, however, other considerations affect the efficiency of the pull.

56. Forces acting on a body lying on a slope.

A smooth ball placed on a smooth horizontal board will rest on it in neutral equilibrium. But if the board be tilted, however slightly, the ball will begin to move.

Gravity is the only force acting which would produce motion. This force acting vertically has no resolved part in a horizontal direction. There is therefore no motion while the board is horizontal. Since it moves when the board is sloped, this must be due to the resolved part of the force of gravity along the sloping surface.

In Fig. 67(a) the diagram shows the forces acting when the ball is at rest on the horizontal surface.   These are :

(1) The weight, *i.e.*, the force of gravity and
(2) the reaction of the board equal and opposite to the forces of gravity, thus producing equilibrium.

In Fig. 67(b) let θ be the angle of slope of the board.
Then the angle between the vertical and the straight line perpendicular to the board is also θ.
$\therefore$ The force W can be resolved into

(1) $W \cos \theta$, acting at right angles to the surface of the board.
(2) $W \sin \theta$, acting along the board.

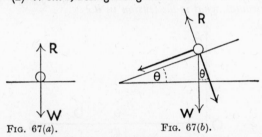

FIG. 67(a).   FIG. 67(b).

It is the resolved part acting down the surface of the board, viz. $W \sin \theta$, which causes the ball to move down the plane.   If there is to be equilibrium in the new position a force equal and opposite to this must act on the body in a direction up the plane.
The reaction of the board will be equal and opposite to the component $W \cos \theta$, acting at right angles to the board.   This reaction is therefore less when the board is tilted than when it is horizontal, and it decreases as θ is increased, since $\cos \theta$ decreases.   At the same time $W \sin \theta$ increases as θ increases.

57. Application of moments to resolved parts.

It was shown in § 50 that the sum of the moments of two intersecting forces about any point in their plane is equal to the moment of their resultant about the same point.

When a force is resolved into two parts, it becomes the resultant of the two components; therefore **the moment of the force about any point is equal to the sum of the moments of its resolved parts.**

This principle is useful in solving problems. An example follows :

58. Worked Example.

A uniform beam OB, 16 ft. long and weighing 150 lbs., is hinged at O (Fig. 68). It is kept in equilibrium in a horizontal position by a wire rope fixed at a point A vertically above O, and attached to the beam at a point D, 12 ft. from O. If the wire makes an angle of 30° with the horizontal, what is the tension in it ?

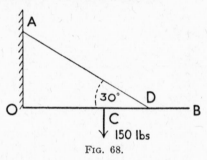

Fig. 68.

The forces acting on the beam are :

(1) The tension, T, in the wire.
(2) Weight of beam at mid point, C.
(3) Reaction at O.

If we take moments about O, that of the reaction, which is unknown, is eliminated.

If T be resolved into its vertical and horizontal components, $T \sin 30°$ and $T \cos 30°$, the latter will pass through O, and therefore has no moment about it.

We are therefore left with :

(1) Vertical component of T, viz. $T \sin 30°$, acting at D.
(2) Weight of beam, 150 lbs. wt., acting at C.

These have opposite turning moments about O, and as there is equilibrium they must be equal.

$$\therefore \quad T \sin 30° \times 12 = 150 \times 8$$
$$T = \frac{150 \times 8}{12 \sin 30°}$$
$$= 200 \text{ lbs. wt.}$$

Exercise 7.

1. A force of 16 lbs. wt. acts along the straight line OA (Fig. 69), which is inclined at an angle of 30° with OX. Find its resolved parts along OX, and OY, which is perpendicular to OX.

2. Find the resolved parts along OX and OY (Fig. 69) when the force along OA is 12 lbs. wt. and the angle AOX is 25°.

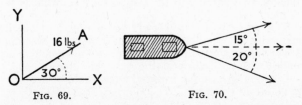

FIG. 69.   FIG. 70.

3. Resolve a force R, of 8 lbs. wt., into two components at right angles and such that one of them makes an angle of 55° with the direction of R.

4. Two tugs are towing a ship. The rope from one of them is inclined at 15° to the path of the ship (Fig. 70) and the other at 20°. If each tug exerts a force equal to the weight of 10 tons, what is the total effective pull in the direction in which the ship is moving?

5. Find the vertical and horizontal resolved parts of the following forces :

(1) A force of 20 lbs. wt., acting at 40° with the horizontal.

(2) A force of 250 grams wt., acting at 30° with the horizontal.

6. A horse, moving along the tow-path, pulls a barge along a canal. The rope by which he pulls is inclined

at 20° to the direction in which the barge is moving. If the horse exerts a force equal to the weight of 400 lbs., what is the pull on the barge in the direction it is moving?

7. A weight of 40 lbs. rests on a smooth surface which is inclined at an angle of 15° to the horizontal (Fig. 71).

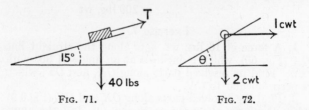

FIG. 71.　　　　　FIG. 72.

If it is just kept in position by a force of T lbs. wt. acting along a rope parallel to the sloping surface, what is the value of T?

8. A force equal to 1 cwt. wt. acting horizontally maintains in equilibrium a cylindrical roller weighing 2 cwt. on a smooth inclined surface which makes an angle θ with the horizontal (Fig. 72). Find the value of θ.

If θ were 45°, what horizontal force would be necessary to maintain the 2 cwt. in equilibrium?

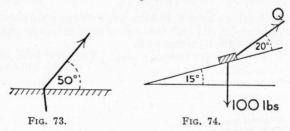

FIG. 73.　　　　　FIG. 74.

9. A stay wire is fastened to a peg embedded in the ground, with which the wire makes an angle of 50° (Fig. 73). If the pull along the wire is equal to the weight of 40 lbs., what vertical force is exerted on the peg to pull it out of the ground?

10. A weight of 100 lbs. rests on a smooth surface inclined to the horizontal at 15°. It is kept in equi-

librium by a force Q which makes an angle of 20° with the inclined surface (Fig. 74).

What is the value of Q?

59. Resolved parts. Resultant of forces acting at a point.

When a number of forces act at a point their resultant can be obtained by resolving the forces along two directions at right angles and then adding these components. The following example will illustrate the method.

Example.—*Two forces P and Q of 8 lbs. and 10 lbs. wt. act along straight lines the angle between which is 45°. Find their resultant.*

Let OA, OB (Fig. 75) be the lines of action of the forces P and Q, the angle between them being 45°.

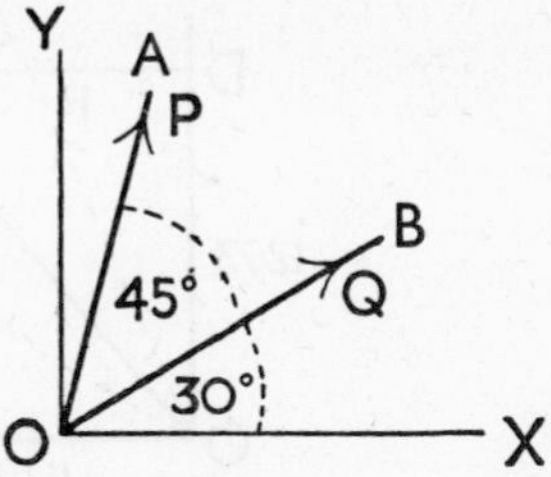

Take two straight lines, OX, OY, at right angles, such that $\angle XOB = 30°$. Then $\angle AOY = 15°$ and $\angle AOX = 75°$.

Note. — Unless straight lines at right angles are specified, OX and OY can be chosen in the way which is most suitable.

Fig. 75.

Find the resolved parts of P and Q along OX and OY:

(1) Resolved parts along OX.

$$Q \cos 30°, P \cos 75°,$$
i.e., $10 \cos 30°, 8 \cos 75°.$

Total $= 10 \cos 30° + 8 \cos 75° = 10 \cdot 73$ lbs. wt. (by calculation not shown).

(2) Resolved parts along OY.

$$Q \sin 30°, P \sin 75°,$$
i.e., $10 \sin 30°, 8 \sin 75°.$

Total. $10 \sin 30° + 8 \sin 75° = 12 \cdot 73$ lbs. wt.

As we have seen (§ 54), these forces represent the total effect of the forces P and Q in these two directions.

∴ The resultant of 10·73 lbs. wt. along *OX* and 12·73 lbs. wt. along *OY* is the same as the resultant of *P* and *Q* (*see* Fig. 76).

∴ if *OE* be measured along *OX*, equal to 10·73, and　*OO*　　　,,　　　*OY*　　,,　12·73, and the rectangle *ODCE* completed, the diagonal of this rectangle, *OC*, represents the resultant.

Let *R* be the resultant.

Then　　　　　$R = \sqrt{(10·73)^2 + (12·73)^2}$
　　　　　　　= 16·7 lbs. wt. nearly (by calculation).

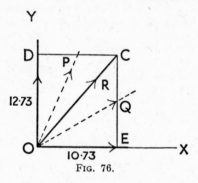
Fig. 76.

If α be the angle made by *R* with *OX*

Then　　　　　$\tan \alpha = \dfrac{12·73}{10·73} = 1·1868,$

and　　　　　$\alpha = 49° 53'.$

60. Resultant of any number of concurrent forces.

This method may not appear to offer much advantage when only two forces are concerned. But it is very valuable when the number of forces is large.

Before proceeding to the general case, it is necessary to consider difficulties which arise when the angles made by the lines of action of the force with either of the axes of reference, *OX* and *OY*, as described in § 59, are greater than right angles.

To simplify the problem we will first consider the case

shown in Fig. 77. A force Q acts at O, and its line of action makes an angle XOB with OX, which with OY at right angles to it are the axes of reference. The angle XOB is greater than a right angle.

It should be remembered that, as in Trigonometry, angles are measured in an anti-clockwise direction, as indicated by the arrow-head on the arc in the diagram.

Let OB represent the magnitude of the force.

Drawing BL perpendicular to OY, OL represents the resolved part of Q along OY, *i.e.*, $Q \sin BOX$.

In order to obtain the resolved part of Q along OX, this line must be produced in the **opposite direction**, *i.e.* along OX'. Then the perpendicular BK from B

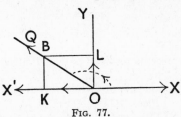

FIG. 77.

cuts off OK, which must represent the resolved part of Q along OX.

$$\therefore \qquad OK = Q \cos BOX.$$

Two points must now be noted :

(1) The cosines of angles between 90° and 180° are negative.

$$\therefore \qquad Q \cos BOX \text{ is negative.}$$

(2) In accordance with the convention of positive and negative directions, when XO is produced in the **opposite** direction from O, distances measured in this direction from O to X' are considered as negative, as contrasted with distances measured from O to X, which are considered positive.

$\therefore$ OK, the resolved part of Q, is negative.

This is in agreement with the statement above that $Q \cos BOX$ is negative, since this is founded on the same convention.

The interpretation of the negative sign in $Q \cos BOX$ is that this force, represented by OK, acts in the opposite direction from forces which act from O towards X.

Let us now consider two forces P and Q acting as shown in Fig. 78, in which OA, OB represent the mag-

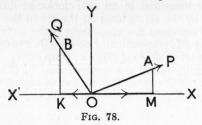

FIG. 78.

nitudes of these forces. Drawing AM and BK perpendicular to XOX'

OM represents resolved part of P along OX.
OK „   „   „ Q „

∴ the algebraic sum of these resolved parts is

$$P \cos AOX - Q \cos BOX$$
$$= OM - OK.$$

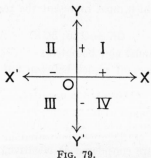

FIG. 79.

61. These principles may be extended to any number of forces which intersect at O.

To include all cases the line OY must also be produced in the opposite direction, so that the axes are drawn as shown in Fig. 79. We thus get four spaces, I, II, III,

IV, which are called quadrants, and the line of action of any force acting at O must fall into one of these.

Using the convention above, measurements along OY' will be negative.

In general :

Resolved parts along OX and OY are positive.

   ,,   ,, OX' and OY' are negative.

As an example, consider the cases of two forces, S and T, falling in the IIIrd and IVth quadrants as shown in Fig. 80.

Let OE, OH represent the magnitudes of S and T.

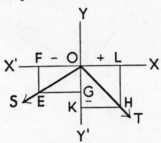

Fig. 80.

Draw perpendiculars to the axes as shown :

   (1) For the force S in Quad. III :

     OF resolved part along OX' is negative.
     OG ,,   ,, OY' is negative.

   (2) For the force T in Quad. IV :

     OL resolved part along OX is positive.
     OK ,,   ,, OY' is negative.

Considering the sum of resolved parts along each axis :

   (1) Along OX. Sum of resolved parts $= OL - OF$.
   (2) Along OY ,,   ,, $= -OG - OK$.

The sum along OX will be positive if $OL > OF$.

  ,,   ,, OY is negative.

All this should offer no difficulty to the student whose knowledge of **Trigonometry** is good. A full treatment from the Trigonometrical point of view will be found in *Trigonometry*, Chapter V.

62. Worked example.

Find the resultant of forces as shown in Fig. 81 :

Viz., 10 *lbs. wt. acting along* OA

	5	,,	,,	OB
	10	,,	,,	OC
	12	,,	,,	OD

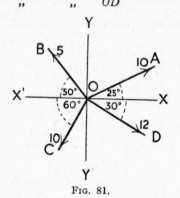

FIG. 81.

the angles made by the lines of action of the forces with *XOX'* and *YOY'* being as shown.

Careful arrangement of the resolved parts is important, and some such tabulation as the following is suggested :

Components along *XOX'*.

	Positive.	Value.	Negative.	Value.
Quad. I	10 cos 25°	9·063		
,, II			5 cos 50°	3·214
,, III			10 cos 60°	5·000
,, IV	12 cos 30°	10·39		
Total	+	19·45	—	8·214

Sum = 11·24 lbs. wt (approx.).

Components along YOY'.

	Positive.	Value.	Negatives.	Value.
Quad. I	10 sin 25°	4·226		
„ II	5 sin 50°	3·830		
„ III			10 sin 60°	8·660
„ IV			12 sin 30°	6·000
Total	+	8·056	—	14·660

Sum $= -6·604$ lbs. wt. (approx.).

The negative sign shows that the total resolved part acts along OY'.

The forces now reduce to two, as shown in Fig. 82.

Completing the rectangle, OA represents the resultant R of the whole system.

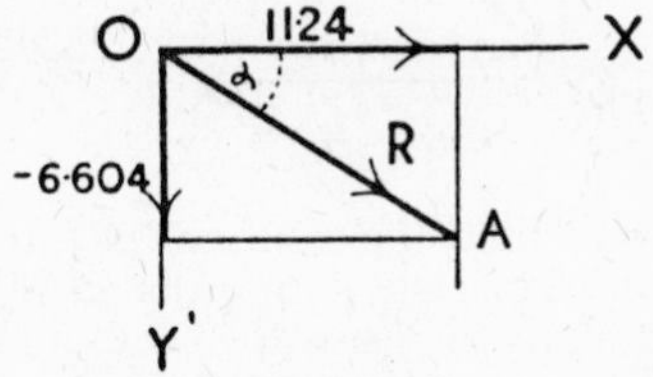

FIG. 82.

To find R:
$$R = \sqrt{(11·24)^2 + (-6·604)^2}$$
$$= \sqrt{170}$$
$$= 13 \text{ lbs. wt. nearly.}$$

Let α be the angle made by the Resultant with OX. Then, taking numerical values only

$$\tan \alpha = \frac{6·604}{11·24} = 0·589 \text{ approx.}$$

$$\therefore \qquad \alpha = 30° 31'.$$

The negative sign, if retained, would show that the angle is in the 4th quadrant (*Trigonometry*, p. 160).

63. Equilibrium of forces acting at a point.

If the resultant of forces acting at a point is zero, the forces are in equilibrium.

Consequently if the sum of the resolved parts in two directions is zero, the resultant must be zero and the forces are in equilibrium.

Exercise 8.

1. Using the method of resolved parts, find the resultant of forces P and Q as shown in Fig. 83.

P is 8 lbs. wt. and makes 45° with OX.
Q ,, 10 ,, ,, 60° ,, OX.

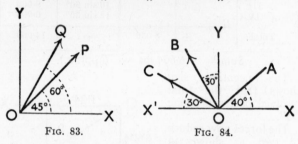

FIG. 83.　　　　　FIG. 84.

2. Find the resultant of forces of 8 lbs. wt., 4 lbs. wt., and 3 lbs. wt., acting along OA, OB, and OC, respectively, making angles with XOX' and OY as shown in Fig. 84. Find also the angle which the resultant makes with XOX'.

3. Forces of 4, 5, 6, and 7 lbs. wt. act at a point O, and the angle between each successive pair is 60° (*see* Fig. 85).

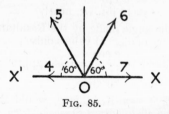

FIG. 85.

Find the resultant and the angle which it makes with OX.

4. $ABCD$ is a square, and forces of 5, 8, 10, and 6 lbs. wt. act at O, the intersection of the diagonals and in the directions of the corners of the squares. Drawing axes of reference as shown in Fig. 86, find the resultant of the forces and its line of action.

5. Three forces of 10, 4, and 5 lbs. wt. act at a point O and make angles with the straight line XOX' as shown in Fig. 87.

Find the resultant and its line of action.

6. Six strings, each string making an angle of 60° with the next string, are attached to a small body. If the tensions in the strings are 1, 2, 3, 4, 5, and 6 units, respectively, find the magnitude and direction of the resultant force on the body.

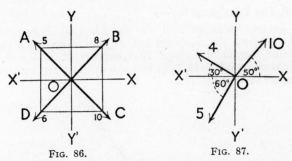

FIG. 86.   FIG. 87.

7. From a point O straight lines OX, OA, OB, OC are drawn so that $\angle XOA = 40°$, $\angle XOB = 120°$, $\angle XOC = 135°$. Forces act along these lines as follows : 12 lbs. wt. along OX, 10 lbs. wt. along OA, 8 lbs. wt. along OB, and 6 lbs. wt. along OC.

Find the resultant of these forces and the angle made by the line of action with OX.

8. Three forces of 10, 8, and 6 lbs. wt. act at a point and the angle between each pair is 120°.

Find the resultant and the angle which it makes with the 10 lbs. wt.

CHAPTER VI

TRIANGLE OF FORCES; POLYGON OF FORCES. LAMI'S THEOREM

64. The Triangle of Forces.

In § 43 an experiment was described which had for its purpose the investigation of the theorem of the Parallelogram of Force. That experiment, in a somewhat different form, may be used to illustrate another aspect of that theorem.

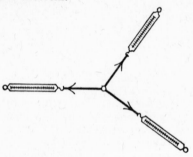

FIG. 88.

Fasten three spring-balances to hooks on a horizontal (or vertical) board. Join them by strings to a small ring so that they are all in tension. Arrange them so that they register different tensions and rest in equilibrium (Fig. 88).

There will thus be three forces, represented by the tensions in the strings, acting on the small ring and in equilibrium.

The tensions in the strings are registered on the spring-balances.

Place a piece of paper under the strings and draw

three lines on it corresponding to the strings. The three lines will, of course, be concurrent at a point corresponding to the small ring.

A diagram will thus be obtained similar to Fig. 89(a), in which the three straight lines which are concurrent at O represent the directions of the three forces P, Q, and R, whose magnitudes are registered on the spring-balances.

Now draw a triangle ABC as in Fig. 89(b), having:

AB parallel to the direction of the force P.
BC   ,,   ,,   ,,   ,, R.
CA   ,,   ,,   ,,   ,, Q.

Space Diagram.   Force Diagram.

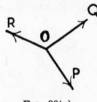 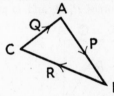

FIG. 89(a).   FIG. 89(b).

These two diagrams are called the Space diagram and the Force diagram, respectively.

Now

    (1) Measure the lengths of the sides of the triangle ABC.
    (2) Find the ratios of the lengths of the sides to the forces to which they are parallel.

i.e., the ratios $\dfrac{P}{AB}, \dfrac{Q}{BC}, \dfrac{R}{CA}.$

It will be found that, with allowances for slight errors, these ratios are equal.

Repeat the experiment with different positions of the spring-balances and different tensions indicated by them.

It will be found that in every case the ratios obtained are equal—*i.e.*:

$$\frac{P}{AB} = \frac{R}{BC} = \frac{Q}{CA}.$$

This may also be expressed thus :

$$\frac{P}{R} = \frac{AB}{BC}.$$

$$\frac{P}{Q} = \frac{AB}{CA}.$$

65. These results can be expressed as follows :

The lengths of the sides of the triangle *ABC* are proportional to the magnitudes of the forces which they represent.

This can also be expressed in the following form:

If the length of *AB* be taken to represent *P*, then the length of *BC*, in the same scale, will represent *R* and the length of *CA* will represent *Q*.

The forces *P*, *Q*, and *R* are in equilibrium, therefore

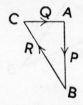

Fig. 90(*a*).
R as Equilibriant.

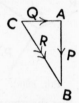

Fig. 90(*b*).
R as Resultant.

the above results may be expressed in general form as follows, the theorem being known as the Triangle of Forces :

The Triangle of Forces.

If three coplanar forces, acting at a point, are in equilibrium, and straight lines be drawn parallel to the directions of the forces, then the lengths of the sides of the triangle so formed are proportional to the magnitudes of the forces which they represent.

66. It should be noted that in Fig. 89(*b*) the directions in which the forces act, as indicated by the arrow-heads on the sides of the triangle, follow the same way round in order : all will be clockwise or all will be anti-clockwise.

If, however, the direction of one of these forces be

reversed, as in 90(b), then this force can be regarded as the resultant.

Thus in Fig. 90(a) the force R maintains equilibrium in conjunction with P and Q and is called the equilibriant.

In Fig. 90(b), the force R, with direction reversed, is the resultant of P and Q.

It corresponds to the diagonal of the parallelogram in the theorem of the parallelogram of forces.

Generally, when three forces acting at a point can be represented in magnitude and direction by the sides of a triangle taken in order, any one of the forces represents either the resultant or equilibriant of the other two, according to the direction in which it acts.

It will be seen that the triangle of force corresponds to the triangle OBC (Fig. 55), which is part of the parallelogram of force, but the method of approach is a converse one.

In the case of the parallelogram of forces two straight lines were drawn which represented two forces in magnitude and direction. It was then found that the third side of a triangle, in the first instance the diagonal of the parallelogram, represented the resultant of these two forces.

But in the triangle of forces experiment it was found that if a triangle was formed whose sides were parallel to the directions only, then the lengths of these sides were proportional to the magnitudes of the forces.

67. The inclined plane.

In § 56 we considered the forces acting on a body resting in equilibrium on a smooth surface inclined to the horizontal. This is usually called an inclined plane. The triangle of force provides a convenient way of representing the forces which act on the body. The following two cases will serve to illustrate the method.

(1) Applied force parallel to the plane.

In Fig. 91 let a body O, weight W, rest on a smooth inclined plane LMN.

Let θ denote ∠LMN, the angle of the slope of the plane.

Let O be held on the plane in equilibrium by a force P acting up the plane .

Then the forces acting on O are :

 (a) W acting vertically downwards.
 (b) P acting parallel to the plane.
 (c) R, the reaction of the plane, perpendicular to the plane.

Since these are in equilibrium, they can be represented by a triangle of force.

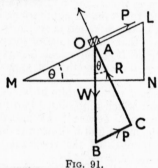

FIG. 91.

To draw the triangle of force.

Produce the line of action of W so that, on a suitable scale, AB represents the force of W lbs. wt.

Draw AC perpendicular to LM.

From B draw BC perpendicular to AC, and therefore parallel to the direction of the force P.

Then the triangle ABC has its sides parallel to the forces acting on O and the ∠BAC = θ.

∴ By the theorem of the triangle of forces, the sides are proportional to the magnitudes of the force W, P, and R.

But AB was drawn to represent the magnitude of W.

∴ With the same scale :

$$AC \text{ represents } R$$
and $$BC \quad \text{,,} \quad P.$$

$$\therefore \qquad \frac{P}{W} = \frac{BC}{AB} = \sin\theta. \qquad \therefore P = W\sin\theta.$$

also $\qquad \dfrac{R}{W} = \dfrac{AC}{AB} = \cos\theta. \qquad \therefore R = W\cos\theta.$

These are the resolved parts of W down the plane and perpendicular to it as shown in § 56.

(2) Applied force acting horizontally.

In this case P acts horizontally and is $\therefore$ at right angles to the direction of W.

The triangle of force, ABC (Fig. 92), is drawn as before, except that BC is drawn perpendicular to AB.

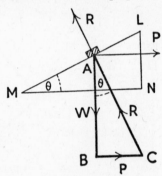

FIG. 92.

Then, as in the last case :

$$AB \text{ represents } W$$
$$AC \quad ,, \quad R$$
$$BC \quad ,, \quad P.$$

Then $\qquad \dfrac{P}{W} = \dfrac{BC}{AB} = \tan\theta. \qquad \therefore P = W\tan\theta.$

$$\frac{R}{W} = \frac{AC}{AB} = \sec\theta. \qquad \therefore R = W\sec\theta.$$

68. Worked Example.

A weight of 20 lbs. suspended by two fine light wires, 5 ft. and 6 ft. in length are fastened to two points A and B,

*which are 8 ft. apart on a horizontal beam (Fig. 93(a)).
The wires are knotted at C. The weight is also fastened
on at C. Find the tension in the wires AC and CB.*

Fig. 93(a) represents the diagram of the arrangement
of the forces according to the data.

CD, the perpendicular from *C* on *AB*, is the continua-
tion of the line of action of the weight of 20 lbs. *P*
and *Q* are the tensions in *CA* and *CB*.

(1) Practical solution.

Construct the triangle of force for the forces *P*, *Q* and
the weight of 20 lbs.

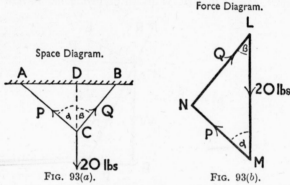

Space Diagram.

Force Diagram.

Fig. 93(a).   Fig. 93(b).

Draw *LM* to represent the 20 lbs., on a suitable scale.
From *M* draw a straight line parallel to *CA* (force *P*).
,,   *L*   ,,   ,,   ,,   *BC* (force *Q*).
Let *N* be the point of intersection of these straight
lines.

Then △*LMN* is the triangle of force and the sides
are proportional to the three forces.

∴ on the same scale that *LM* represents 20 lbs. wt.

MN will represent the tension *P*.
NL   ,,   ,,   ,,   *Q*.

(2) Trigonometrical solution.

We must solve the △*LMN*, knowing that *LM* represents 20 lbs.

Then we can calculate the lengths of LN and MN.

From the properties of parallel lines the angles α and β as shown in the triangle of force are equal to α and β as shown in the space diagram.

To find α and β we must first solve $\triangle ABC$, knowing all the sides.

Applying the cosine rule (*Trigonometry*, § 102) :

$$\cos A = \frac{8^2 + 6^2 - 5^2}{2 \cdot 8 \cdot 6},$$

whence $\qquad A = 38° 37',$

and $\qquad \alpha = 90° - A = 51° 23'.$

Similarly $\quad \cos B = \frac{8^2 + 5^2 - 6^2}{2 \cdot 8 \cdot 5}$

and $\qquad B = 48° 30'.$

∴ $\qquad \beta = 90 - B = 41° 30'.$

Also $\quad \angle LNM = 180° - (\alpha + \beta) = 87° 7'.$

To find the sides of $\triangle LMN$ we use the sine rule (*Trigonometry*, § 90).

$$\frac{LN}{20} = \frac{\sin 51° 23'}{\sin 87° 7'},$$

whence $\qquad LN = 15 \cdot 6$ (approx.),

$$\frac{MN}{20} = \frac{\sin 41° 30'}{\sin 87° 7'},$$

whence $\qquad MN = 13 \cdot 3$ (approx.).

∴ $\qquad Q = 15 \cdot 6$ lbs. wt.

$\qquad P = 13 \cdot 3$ lbs. wt.

69. Lami's Theorem.

Trigonometrical solutions of problems involving the triangle of forces are frequently made easier by using the theorem below :

Fig. 94(*a*) represents the directions of three forces, P, Q, R, in equilibrium.

Fig. 94(*b*) represents the $\triangle$ of force corresponding to these forces.

If, with the usual notation, a, b, c represent the sides of $\triangle ABC$, opposite respectively to the angles $A, B, C,$

then by the theorem of the Triangle of Force, the lengths of these sides are proportional to the forces P, Q, R.

$$\therefore \qquad \frac{P}{a} = \frac{Q}{b} = \frac{R}{c} \qquad . \quad . \quad . \quad . \quad (1)$$

Using the sine rule (Trig., § 90) for the $\triangle ABC$.

$$\frac{a}{\sin A} = \frac{b}{\sin B} = \frac{c}{\sin C}.$$

Let each of these ratios $= k$.

$$\textit{I.e.,} \qquad \frac{a}{\sin A} = \frac{b}{\sin B} = \frac{c}{\sin C} = k.$$

$$\therefore \qquad \begin{aligned} a &= k \sin A \\ b &= k \sin B \\ c &= k \sin C \end{aligned}$$

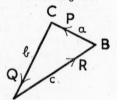

Space Diagram.   Force Diagram.

Fig. 94(a).   Fig. 94(b).

Substituting these for a, b, c in (1) above, we have

$$\frac{P}{k \sin A} = \frac{Q}{k \sin B} = \frac{R}{k \sin C}.$$

As these are all equal, if each be multiplied by k the results are equal.

$$\therefore \qquad \frac{P}{\sin A} = \frac{Q}{\sin B} = \frac{R}{\sin C}.$$

Comparing with the space diagram:

$$\begin{aligned} &\angle A \text{ and } \angle A' \text{ are, supplementary} \\ &\angle B \quad ,, \quad \angle B' \quad ,, \qquad ,, \\ &\angle C \quad ,, \quad \angle C' \quad ,, \qquad ,, \end{aligned}$$

and the sine of an angle is equal to the sine of its supplement.

$$\therefore \qquad \frac{P}{\sin A'} = \frac{Q}{\sin B'} = \frac{R}{\sin C'},$$

where A' is the angle between Q and R,

B' " " " P and R,

C' " " " P and Q.

This is the theorem known as :

Lami's Theorem.

If three forces acting at a point are in equilibrium, each is proportional to the sine of the angle included between the other two.

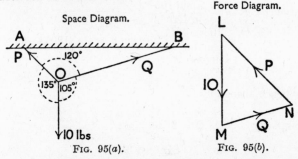

Space Diagram.

Force Diagram.

Fig. 95(a).   Fig. 95(b).

This theorem is named after Bernard Lami, who enunciated it in his *Traité de Mechanique*, published in 1687.

70. Worked Example.

A weight of 10 lbs. is supported by two strings OA, OB, knotted at O and attached at A and B to a horizontal beam. The angle between the strings is 120° (see Fig. 95(a)), that between OA and the vertical string holding the weight is 135° and that between OB and the vertical string is 105°. Find the tensions in the strings OA and OB.

Let P, Q represent the tensions in OA and OB.

Construct the triangle of force by drawing

LM parallel to vertical string and representing 10 lbs.

MN parallel to OB.

LN parallel to AO.

(1) Drawing solution.

A solution can be obtained by drawing the triangle of force to a suitable scale and making LM 10 units in length to represent the weight.

The lengths of LN and MN in the scale chosen give the values of P and Q.

(2) Solution using Lami's Theorem.

By this theorem :

$$\frac{P}{\sin 105°} = \frac{Q}{\sin 135°} = \frac{10}{\sin 120°}.$$

whence $P = \dfrac{10 \times \sin 105°}{\sin 120°}$

$= \dfrac{10 \sin 75°}{\sin 60°}$ (since $\sin \theta = \sin (180° - \theta)$)

$= \dfrac{9·659}{0·8660}.$

Whence, using logs

$$P = 11·15 \text{ lbs. wt.}$$

Similarly $\qquad Q = 8·166 \text{ lbs. wt.}$

Exercise 9.

1. The sides of a triangle are parallel to the lines of action of three forces in equilibrium, and are 8, 10, and 12 cms. long. The force to which the longest side is parallel is 20 lbs. wt. What are the other forces?

2. P, Q, and R are three forces in equilibrium; P is 10 lbs. wt., Q is 15 lbs. wt. In the triangle of force which represents them, the side parallel to the direction of Q is 3·75 ins. and the side parallel to the direction of R is 4·5 ins. Find R and the length of the side parallel to P.

3. A 28-lb. wt. is supported by two cords, one of which makes an angle of 60° with the vertical. What must be the direction of the second cord so that the tension may be the least possible?

Find the tension in the two cords in this case.

4. A metal cylinder of weight 3 lbs. lies on a smooth

plane inclined at 35° to the horizontal, and is kept in equilibrium by a force of P lbs. wt. acting along a string which is parallel to the plane. Construct a triangle of force corresponding to these forces, and from it find the tension in the string and the reaction of the plane.

Check by calculating the values of the forces.

5. A body weighing 5 lbs. is kept at rest on an inclined plane of angle 30°, by a horizontal string. Construct the corresponding triangle of force, and from it determine the tension in the string and the reaction of the plane.

Also calculate the values of these two forces.

6. Three forces P, Q, and R, act at a point and are in equilibrium. P is 20 lbs. wt. The angle between P and Q is 105° and that between P and R is 120°. Find the forces Q and R.

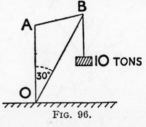

FIG. 96.

7. Two strings, AB and AC, are fastened to a horizontal beam at B and C. They are knotted at A to a third string, which hangs vertically and sustains a weight of 10 lbs. AB and AC make angles of 50° and 60° on either side of the vertical through A. Find the tensions in AB and AC.

8. OB (Fig. 96) represents the jib of a crane, and from B is suspended a load of 10 tons. OB makes an angle of 30° with the vertical, and AB is a tie rod. OA is 10 ft. in length and OB is 12 ft.

Find the tensions in OB and AB, either by drawing or by the use of Lami's Theorem.

71. The Polygon of Forces.

We have seen that if three forces acting at a point are in equilibrium they can be represented by the sides of a triangle in accordance with the Triangle of Forces. This principle can be extended to any number of forces.

Let forces P, Q, R, S, and T, whose magnitudes are known and which act at a point O (Fig. 97(a)), be in equilibrium, their directions being indicated in the figure by the straight lines as marked.

(1) Taking any point A (Fig. 97(b)), draw AB to represent P in magnitude and parallel to its direction.

(2) From B draw BC to represent Q in magnitude and parallel to its direction.

Then ABC is a $\triangle$ of force and AC represents the resultant of P and Q in magnitude and direction.

(3) From C draw CD to represent R in magnitude and parallel to its direction.

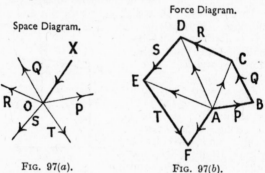

Space Diagram.

Force Diagram.

FIG. 97(a). FIG. 97(b).

Then ACD is a $\triangle$ of force for R and AC which is the resultant of P and Q; AD is $\therefore$ the resultant of AC and CD.

Then AD represents the resultant of $P + Q + R$ in magnitude and direction.

(4) From D draw DE to represent S in magnitude and direction.

Then, as in the other cases :

AE represents the resultant of $P + Q + R + S$ in magnitude and direction.

(5) From E draw EF to represent T in magnitude and direction.

Then AF represents the resultant of AE and EF.

$\therefore$ AF represents the resultant of $P + Q + R + S + T$ in magnitude and direction.

I.e., *AF* represents in magnitude and is parallel to the direction of the resultant of the system of forces acting at *O*.

∴ if from *O* in Fig. 97(*a*) we draw *OX* parallel to *AF* and of the same length it will represent the resultant of the forces concurrent at *O*.

Since *AF* represents the resultant of the five forces, then the force which it represents in magnitude, with the direction reversed—*i.e.*, *FA*—if applied at *O* would represent the equilibriant of the five forces, and the system will be in equilibrium.

This is the theorem known as the Polygon of Forces, and it may be defined as follows :

Polygon of Force.

If a number of forces acting at a point are in equilibrium, they can be represented in magnitude and direction by the sides of a polygon, taken in order.

For example, four forces acting at a point and in equilibrium
can be represented by the sides
of a quadrilateral.

It should be noted that the
words " taken in order " in the
definition above mean, as in

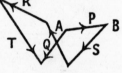

FIG. 98.

the case of the triangle of force, that the direction of the forces going round the polygon is the same, all the arrowheads pointing clockwise or anti-clockwise.

If this condition be fulfilled, the forces can be drawn in any order, so that the same polygon of force may have different shapes.

Thus in the example above the polygon might be drawn as in Fig. 98. Starting from *A*, the sequence of forces is *P*, *S*, *Q*, *R*, *T*, all of which follow the same order round. Then, as in all cases :

The force which closes the polygon is the Resultant or Equilibriant according to the sense in which it acts.

In working problems the unknown force should be

drawn last. Then it closes the polygon and its direction and magnitude are determined.

72. Worked Example.

Find by means of a Polygon of Force the resultant of four forces of 4 lbs. wt., 3 lbs. wt., 3 lbs. wt., and 4 lbs. wt., acting as shown in Fig. 99.

To draw the Polygon of Force.

From a suitable point A draw AB, parallel to Q and equal to 3 units of length.

Then in succession draw :

$$BC \text{ parallel to } P,$$
$$CD \quad ,, \quad S,$$
$$DE \quad ,, \quad R.$$

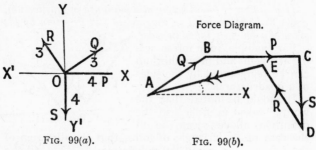

Space Diagram.

FIG. 99(*a*).

Force Diagram.

FIG. 99(*b*).

All must be drawn to the scale adopted for Q.

Join EA.

Then EA represents the Resultant.

Its length is 5·13.

∴ Resultant is 5·13 lbs. wt.

The angle made with OX is given by the angle EAX in the Force diagram. It is about 12°.

The result may be checked using the method of § 62.

Taking the resolved parts we get a total of

$$5 \cdot 098 \text{ lbs. wt. along } OX,$$
$$1 \cdot 098 \quad ,, \quad ,, \quad OY.$$

(*See* Fig. 100.)

$$\therefore \text{ Resultant } = \sqrt{5 \cdot 098^2 + 1 \cdot 098^2}$$
$$= 5 \cdot 13 \text{ approx.}$$

and
$$\tan \alpha = \frac{1 \cdot 098}{5 \cdot 098} = \tan 12° \, 8'.$$

$$\therefore \qquad\qquad \alpha = 12° \, 8'.$$

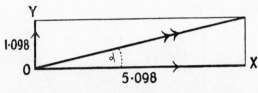

Fig. 100.

Exercise 10.

1. Forces represented by $OA = 8$ lbs. wt., $OB = 10$ lbs. wt., and $OC = 5$ lbs. wt., all acting at a point O, are separated by angles as shown in Fig. 101. Find graphically their resultant and the angle which it makes with OX.

2. Four forces act at a point O as shown in Fig. 102. Find the resultant and the angle which it makes with OX.

3. Three forces, $P = 30$ lbs. wt., $Q = 40$ lbs. wt., and

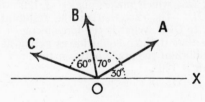

Fig. 101.

$R = 50$ lbs. wt., act at a point. The angle between P and Q is $45°$ and that between Q and R is $60°$. Find the magnitude of the resultant graphically and by calculation.

4. Forces of 8 lbs. wt., 5 lbs. wt., 10 lbs. wt., and 8 lbs.

wt. act at a point and in directions as shown in Fig. 103. Find the resultant and the angle which it makes with the direction of the 5 lbs. force.

5. Three forces pass through a point in a body and act outwards. The forces are A, of 5 lbs. wt., B, of 10 lbs. wt. acting at 60° to A, and C, of 15 lbs. wt. at 210° to A, measured in the same direction. Is the body in

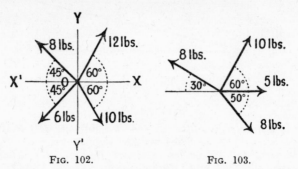

FIG. 102.   FIG. 103.

equilibrium? If not what is the resultant of the forces, and what single force will produce equilibrium?

The problem may be solved graphically.

6. Forces of 2 lbs. wt. and 4 lbs. wt. act along OA and OB, and the angle between them is 120°. A third force acts along OC, which makes angles of 120° with both OA and OB. The direction of the resultant is perpendicular to OB. What is the force along OC?

7. Show that if three equal forces acting at a point are in equilibrium the angle between the lines of action of each pair is 120°.

CHAPTER VII

FRICTION

73. Friction as a force.

When considering problems connected with forces which act on bodies moving or lying on surfaces, or cords passing over pulleys, we have assumed that the surfaces were smooth. By this assumption the problems were not complicated by the forces brought into play when surfaces are not smooth.

It is common experience that all surfaces are rough to a greater or less degree, and that, in consequence, there is resistance to motion over them.

If a body is resting on a horizontal plane, the only forces acting on it to keep it in equilibrium are :

(1) Its weight acting vertically downwards,
(2) The reaction of the surface, equal and opposite to the weight.

Neither of these forces can have any resolved part at right angles to itself, and consequently have no effect in a horizontal direction.

The resistance to horizontal motion, which we know from experience is brought into play, must be due to the force, which is called the force of friction.

This force may be very useful, even essential, or it may be the reverse. Without it, walking and running would be very difficult, as we know if we try to move on a surface which is smooth and offers very little resistance, such as ice. But for the parts of moving machinery we employ metals with surfaces as smooth as possible to minimise friction.

Without friction the wheels of a locomotive or of a motor would spin round rapidly, without any progress being made; but the hull of a fast liner or the skin of an aeroplane are made as smooth as possible, so as to reduce frictional resistance to a minimum.

It is necessary, then, to investigate the action of the resistance due to friction, and to know how to measure it.

74. Limiting friction.

For the measurement of this force we must rely on experiments.

Experiment. A block of wood of known weight, W lbs., is placed on a wooden table (Fig. 104). As it lies on the table, the forces acting on it, as stated above, are:

(1) Its **weight, W**, acting vertically downwards.

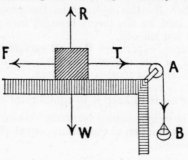

Fig. 104.

(2) The **reaction** of the table, R, equal and opposite to W.

A light cord is attached to the block, and carried over a small smooth pulley, A, to a scale-pan B, whose weight is known.

A small weight is placed in the scale-pan. This introduces a new force, which, together with the weight of the scale-pan, acts vertically downwards. It thus sets up a tension in the string which is transmitted, practically unaltered, and acts horizontally on the block.

If the weight be small, the block will not move.

Consequently a force must have been brought into action—the force of friction—which acts horizontally, and, since there is no motion, is equal and opposite to T. Thus we conclude that the force of friction begins to act only when there is a pull in the cord (T), and ceases when the pull ceases.

We now add more weights gradually to the scale-pan: T is thus increased, and so long as there is no motion the force of friction is also increased, so as to equal T.

As we continue to increase the weights in the pan, a time will come when the block will just begin to move. At that moment the two forces are equal, but with a slight increase in T the block moves.

Thus the force of friction will increase up to a certain amount, and no more.

There is therefore a limit-ing value of the force of friction beyond which it cannot increase, and the body will not move until the force applied to move the body (T) is greater than it.

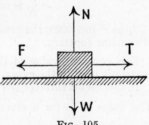

Fig. 105.

75. Coefficient of friction.

Let F be the limiting value of friction in the above experiment.

Let N be the normal reaction of the board on the block. Then the forces acting on the block in the experiment are (see Fig. 105):

(1) Vertically:
   W, the weight downwards.
   N, the reaction upwards.

(2) Horizontally:
   T, the pull of the scale-pan.
   F, force of friction opposite in direction to T.

As there is equilibrium

$$F = T.$$

Continuing the experiment place additional weights on the top of the block.

Then it will be found that more weights must be

placed on the pan until the point is reached when the block is again about to move :

i.e., as   W increases,
                F also increases.

As further weights are added, both increase, but in every case it will be found that, with slight errors, the ratio :

$$\frac{F}{W} \text{ is constant.}$$

Also $W = N$ throughout the experiments.

∴ $\frac{F}{N}$ is constant.

∴ as F increases, the ratio of F to the normal reaction N remains constant.

This constant value of the ratio applies only to the materials used in the experiment.

If two metal surfaces were used it would be different. The value of $\frac{F}{N}$ for a given pair of surfaces is usually denoted by the Greek letter μ (pronounced " mew ").

We can therefore write :

$$\frac{F}{N} = \mu,$$
or $F = \mu N.$

In another form this means:

The limiting value of the force of friction for any two substances is equal to the total normal reaction multiplied by μ.

The constant μ is called the coefficient of friction. Values of μ.

The following are values of μ for a few substances.

Wood on wood 0·35 if polished, to 0·5 if dry.
Wood on metal 0·10 if polished, to 0·6.
Metal on metal 0·15 to 0·18.
Metal on metal (if greased) 0·1.
Wood on stone 0·6.
Leather on wood 0·62.

As indicated above, the constant μ may vary for two substances, according to the degree of polish of the surfaces.

It does not depend on the areas of the surfaces in contact.

A smooth surface is one whose coefficient of friction is zero or is so small as to be negligible.

76. The angle of friction.

The results of the last paragraph showed the relation between :

(1) the limiting friction, F,
and (2) the normal reaction,

viz., $$\frac{F}{N} = \mu.$$

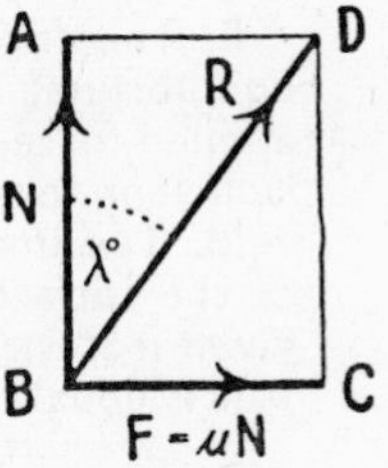

The resultant of these two forces F and N can be found by means of the parallelogram of forces. As the two forces are at right angles, the parallelogram will be a rectangle.

FIG. 106.

In Fig. 106 :

$$AB \text{ represents } N,$$
$$BC \quad ,, \quad F = \mu N.$$
$$\therefore \quad BD \quad ,, \quad R, \text{ the resultant.}$$

Let the angle between N and R be denoted by λ (pronounced "lambda").

Then $$\tan \lambda = \frac{F}{N}$$
$$= \frac{\mu N}{N}$$
$$= \mu.$$

The angle λ is called the **angle of friction**.

Thus, *the angle of friction is the angle whose tangent is equal to the coefficient of friction*

or $$\lambda = \tan^{-1} \mu.$$

77. Kinetic friction.

When motion takes place, the friction, in general, is less than the limiting friction, which tends to prevent motion. This is called " kinetic friction ", and it depends on the velocity at which the body moves.

78. The laws of friction.

From the conclusions reached above we may formulate the laws of friction as follows :

I. Friction acts in an opposite direction to that in which a body tends to move.

II. The force of friction varies, while there is equilibrium, according to the magnitude of the applied force, but cannot exceed that which is just sufficient to prevent the body from moving.

III. The limiting friction depends on the nature of the surfaces in contact but is constant for two given materials.

It is equal to the ratio

$$\frac{\text{total horizontal reaction}}{\text{total normal reaction}}$$

and is denoted by μ.

IV. The coefficient of friction is independent of the areas in contact.

V. If a body rests on a surface the *resultant* reaction of the surface on the body is inclined to the vertical at an angle λ, such that $\tan \lambda = \mu$.

79. Action on a body about to move on a horizontal surface by a force inclined to the surface.

Let a wooden block, weight W, resting on a horizontal surface (Fig. 107) be acted upon by a force P, inclined to horizontal at angle θ.

Let N be the normal reaction.

Then $N = W$.

Let F be the force of friction acting horizontally when the body is on the point of moving.

Then $F = \mu N$.

Let R be the resultant of N and F.

Then R is inclined at angle λ to the vertical (§ 76), so that

$$\tan \lambda = \mu.$$

Replacing N and F by their resultant, the forces acting on the block are as shown in Fig. 108(a).

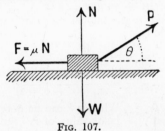

FIG. 107.

The triangle of force for these forces is shown in Fig 108(b) and is drawn as follows :

(1) Draw AB to represent the magnitude and direction of W, which is known.

(2) Draw BC parallel to R—*i.e.*, making an angle $\lambda°$ with the vertical.

(3) Draw AC parallel to P, making $90° - \theta$ with the vertical and meeting BC in C.

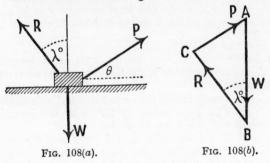

FIG. 108(a).   FIG. 108(b).

Then on the scale that AB represents W :

AC will represent the magnitude of P,

and $\qquad BC \qquad ,, \qquad ,, \qquad ,, \qquad R.$

A graphical solution can thus be obtained.

Trigonometrical solution.

To determine P, the triangle ABC must be solved.

Now $\angle ACB = 180° - (\angle BAC + \angle ABC)$
       $= 180° - (90° - \theta + \lambda)$,

but $\sin \alpha = \sin (180° - \alpha)$.   (*Trigonometry*, § 70.)

∴ $\sin ACB = \sin (90° - \theta + \lambda)$.

Since θ and λ are known, we can thus find ACB.
Using the sine rule :

$$\frac{P}{\sin \lambda} = \frac{W}{\sin ACB}.$$

∴ $$\frac{P}{\sin \lambda} = \frac{W}{\sin (90° - \theta + \lambda)}.$$

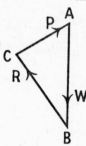

FIG. 109.

Whence P can be determined.

Least value of P. Since P is represented by AC in the Triangle of Force, P will have its least value when AC is least—*i.e.*, when AC is perpendicular to BC. Then the Triangle of Force is as shown in Fig. 109.

Then $$\frac{P}{W} = \sin \lambda.$$

∴ $P = W \sin \lambda.$

∴ The least value of P is $W \sin \lambda$, when the angle which it makes with the horizontal is λ.

80. Worked example.

A metal block weighing 20 lbs. rests on a horizontal board, and the coefficient of friction between the surfaces is 0·22. Find :

(1) *The horizontal force which will just move the block.*

(2) *The force acting at 30° with the horizontal which will just move the block.*

(3) *The least value of the force inclined to the horizontal which will just move the block.*

(1) The horizontal force which will just move the block, as shown in § 75, is given by:

$F = \mu N$

and $N = W.$

$\therefore \qquad\qquad F = \mu W = 0.22 \times 20$
$$= 4.4 \text{ lbs. wt.}$$

(2) When F makes 30° with the horizontal the forces acting are as shown in Fig. 110(a) (*see* § 79).

To find λ:

$$\tan \lambda = \mu$$
$$= 0.22.$$
$\therefore \qquad\qquad \lambda = 12° 24'.$

To draw the Triangle of Force (Fig. 110(b)) :

(1) Draw AB vertical to represent 20.

(2) From B draw BC parallel to R—*i.e.*, $\angle B = 12° 24'$.

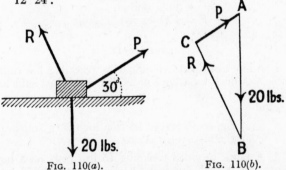

FIG. 110(a).   FIG. 110(b).

(3) From A draw AC parallel to P—*i.e.*, making 30° with the horizontal and meeting BC in C.

Then AC represents P and can be found from a drawing to scale.

Trigonometrical solution.

The $\triangle ABC$ must be solved as shown in § 79.

$\qquad \angle ACB = 180° - (60° + 12° 24')$
$$= 180° - 72° 24'.$$
$\therefore \sin ACB = \sin 72° 24'. \qquad$ (Supplementary angles.)

Using the sine rule.

$$\frac{P}{\sin 12° 24'} = \frac{20}{\sin 72° 24'}.$$
$\therefore \qquad\qquad P = \frac{20 \times \sin 12° 24'}{\sin 72° 24'}.$

$\therefore \log P = \log 20 + \log \sin 12° 24'$
$\qquad - \log \sin 72° 24'$
$\qquad = \log 0·6537.$
$\therefore \qquad P = 4·505$
or $\qquad P = 4·5$ lbs. wt. nearly.

No.	log.
20	1·3010
sin 12° 24'	$\bar{1}$·3319
	0·6329
sin 72° 24'	$\bar{1}$·9792
4·505	0·6537

(3) Least value of P.

As shown in § 78, the least value of P will occur when in the triangle of force AC is perpendicular to BC.
Then $\qquad P = 20 \sin \lambda$
$\qquad\qquad = 20 \times \sin 12° 24'$
$\qquad\qquad = 20 \times 0·2147.$
$\therefore \qquad\qquad P = 4·29$ lbs. wt. approx.

Exercise 11.

1. A block of wood weighing 6 lbs. rests on a horizontal table. A horizontal force of 2·5 lbs. wt. is just sufficient to cause it to slide.
Find

      (a) the coefficient of friction for the two surfaces;
      (b) the angle of friction.

2. A block of wood weighing 15 lbs. rests on a horizontal table and can just be moved along by a force equal to 4·2 lbs. Another 6 lbs. is placed on the block. What is the least horizontal force which will just move the block?

3. A body weighing 12 lbs. rests on a horizontal table and the coefficient of friction between the two surfaces is 0·32. What horizontal force will be required to start the body moving?

4. A block of wood weighing 5 lbs. rests on a horizontal surface and the angle of friction between the two surfaces is 14°. What is the least force which will just cause the block to slide along the surface?

5. A block of wood resting on a horizontal table is just moved by a horizontal force of 15 lbs. wt. If the coefficient of friction between the table and the block is 0·35, find the weight of the block.

6. A block of wood weighing 5 lbs. rests on a rough horizontal board and the coefficient of friction between the surfaces is 0·4. By means of a string inclined at 30° to the board, a pull is exerted on the block which is just sufficient to make it move. Calculate the amount of the pull.

7. A block weighing 40 lbs. is pulled very slowly along a horizontal plane, the coefficient of friction being 0·2. Find the magnitude of the pull if its line of action is (1) horizontal; (2) at 45°; (3) such that the pull is a minimum.

8. A uniform ladder rests at an angle of 45° against a smooth vertical wall. Show that the coefficient of friction between the foot of the ladder and the ground (supposed horizontal) must be at least ½.

9. A block of wood weighing 20 lbs. rests on a horizontal table, and the coefficient of friction between the surfaces is 0·5. Find the force, acting at 45° with the horizontal, which will just move the weight.

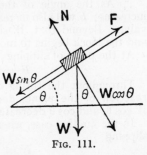

Fig. 111.

81. The inclined plane and friction.

The inclined plane provides an easy way of observing the laws of friction. When the forces acting on a body lying on an inclined plane were considered (§ 67) it was assumed that the plane was smooth. We must now see how these forces are affected when friction is taken into account.

Experiment. Take a board and place on it a wooden block, such as was used in the experiment described in § 74.

Tilt the board slowly through a small angle θ.

The weight (W) of the block can now be resolved into components:

$W \sin \theta$ acting along and down the plane.

$W \cos \theta$ acting perpendicular to the plane.

If the angle of tilting (θ) is small the block will not slide down the plane but will remain at rest.

$\therefore$ The component of the weight down the plane, $W \sin \theta$, must be counteracted by a force acting along and up the plane.

This must be the force of friction, denoted by F.

Now $\sin \theta$ increases as θ increases.

$\therefore$ As the board is tilted a little more, $W \sin \theta$ will increase, and consequently the counterbalancing force of friction, F, must increase.

But as in the case of a body resting on a horizontal surface, this force of friction has a limiting value, beyond which it cannot increase.

$\therefore$ As the angle of the plane is increased $W \sin \theta$ increases; F will also increase until it reaches its limiting value. Beyond that, $W \sin \theta$ becomes greater than F and the block begins to move down the plane.

At the point of slipping

$$F = W \sin \theta \quad . \quad . \quad . \quad . \quad (1)$$

Throughout the tilting of the plane, N, the normal reaction of the plane, decreases, since it is equal to $W \cos \theta$, and $\cos \theta$ decreases as θ increases.

In the limiting case, when the block is on the point of slipping

$$N = W \cos \theta \quad . \quad . \quad . \quad . \quad (2)$$

From equations (1) and (2) :

$$\frac{F}{N} = \frac{W \sin \theta}{W \cos \theta} = \tan \theta.$$

$\therefore \qquad \dfrac{F}{N} = \tan \theta.$

In the limit θ becomes the angle of friction for the two materials and may be replaced by λ.

$\therefore \qquad \dfrac{F}{N} = \tan \lambda$

$\qquad\qquad = \mu.$

$\therefore \qquad F = \mu N.$

In this way the angle of friction, and therefore μ, is easily found by direct observation of the angle of the plane.

Note.—When solving problems connected with the inclined plane and involving the force of friction, the student should note the following two points :

(1) **The force of friction always opposes motion.** Consequently if a body is on the point of slipping down the plane, the force of friction acts up the plane and vice versa.

(2) If a force acting on a body on an inclined plane is inclined to the plane, then it has resolved parts along and perpendicular to the plane. The latter produces a reaction of the plane, and as the force of friction applies to the **total normal reaction** of the plane, it applies to the resolved part of the force which is perpendicular to the plane.

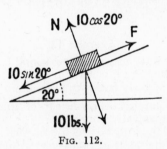

Fig. 112.

Worked Example.

A body weighing 10 lbs. is on the point of slipping down a plane which is inclined at 20° to the horizontal. What force parallel to the plane will just move it up the plane?

As the body is just on the point of slipping down the plane, the angle of the plane is equal to the angle of friction,

i.e., $\lambda = 20°,$

and $\mu = \tan \lambda = \tan 20°.$

When the body is on the point of moving **up** the plane, the forces opposing motion are:

(1) Resolved part of weight,
$$W \sin \theta = 10 \sin 20°.$$

(2) Limiting value of friction, which is μN, where $N = W \cos \theta = 10 \cos 20°$.

$\therefore \qquad \mu N = \mu \times 10 \cos 20°.$

The force necessary just to move the body up the plane must be equal to the sum of those acting down the plane.

$$\therefore \qquad F = W \sin \theta + \mu W \cos \theta$$
$$= 10 \sin 20° + \mu \times 10 \cos 20°,$$

but $\qquad \mu = \tan 20°.$

$$\therefore \quad F = 10 \sin 20° + 10 \tan 20° \times \cos 20°$$
$$= 10 \sin 20° + 10 \times \frac{\sin 20°}{\cos 20°} \times \cos 20°$$
$$= 10 \sin 20° + 10 \sin 20°$$
$$= 20 \sin 20° = 20 \times 0·3420$$
$$= 6·84 \text{ lbs. wt.}$$

Exercise 12.

1. A body rests on a rough horizontal board. This is gradually tilted until, when it is inclined at 22° to the horizontal, the body begins to move down the plane.

(1) What is the coefficient of friction between the body and the plane?
(2) If the body weighs 5 lbs., what is the magnitude of the force of friction when the body begins to slip?

2. A block of wood rests on an inclined plane and the coefficient of friction between it and the plane is known to be 0·31. At what angle must the plane be inclined to the horizontal so that the block begins to move down the plane?

3. A mass of 50 lbs. rests on a rough slope, inclined at 20° to the horizontal. The least force directed up the plane which will move the mass is 56 lbs. wt. Find:

(1) the angle of friction;
(2) the least force directed down the plane which will move the mass.

4. A body weighing 5 lbs. rests on a plane inclined at

40° to the horizontal. It is kept from slipping down the plane by a force equal to the weight of 1·5 lbs. What is the coefficient of friction?

5. A body weighing 40 lbs. is lying on an inclined plane, the slope of which is 30° and is on the point of slipping down the plane. What force applied parallel to the plane will cause the block to begin moving up the plane?

6. A load of 50 lbs. resting on a rough inclined plane begins to slip when the plane is tilted to an angle of 30° with the horizontal. What force up the plane will be necessary to keep the load from slipping down the plane if the angle of slope is increased to 45°?

7. In the last question what force would be necessary to make the body begin moving up the plane?

8. What horizontal force must be applied to the load in question 6, so that it will just begin to move up the plane?

CHAPTER VIII

BODIES IN MOTION ; VELOCITY

82. In the preceding chapters we have confined our attention to the consideration of bodies at rest under the action of force. We now proceed to the study of the " Dynamics " section of the subject—that is, to the consideration of bodies in motion and of the laws relating to motion.

Motion of a body means that its position is changed; it is displaced. This takes place under the action of force and, as will be learnt later, in the direction of the line of action of the force. Thus, bodies falling under the action of the force of gravity tend to fall vertically downwards. Displacement therefore involves magnitude and direction. It is thus a vector quantity (*see* § 41).

83. Speed and velocity.

When a body is in motion the rate at which it is moving on its path is called its speed or velocity.

In everyday language these two terms are usually accepted as meaning the same thing, and by some writers on mechanics they are treated as alternatives. A distinction, however, is usually made between them. While speed is defined as the rate only at which a body is moving, the term velocity implies direction as well as rate.

Speed is certainly frequently used in a sense which has no reference whatever to direction. Thus, an aeroplane may be described as capable of a speed of " 400 miles per hour ", whereas the term velocity is more appropriately used in such a statement as " the wind was blowing with a velocity of 50 miles per hour in a direction N.N.E."

This is a clear and logical distinction and its adoption means that

> speed is a scalar quantity, involving magnitude only, whereas
> velocity is a vector quantity, involving direction as well as magnitude.

84. Units in the measurement of speed and velocity.

If speed is the rate at which a body is moving, this rate must involve

(1) the distance it moves and
(2) the time taken.

Therefore the units employed in measuring speed or velocity must be in terms of the units of distance and the units of time.

Speed may be expressed either in large units such as miles and hours, or in small units such as feet and seconds.

Thus we may speak of a speed of 400 miles per hour, usually written as 400 m.p.h., or of a speed of 20 feet per second, written as 20 ft./sec.

Other units of distance may be similarly employed.

For nautical purposes the unit employed is the knot, which includes both distance and time, for

$$1 \text{ knot} = 1 \text{ nautical mile per hour.}$$

A nautical mile = 6080 ft.

We frequently require to change rates expressed in certain units to those expressed in other units—for examples, miles per hour to feet per second. The connection in this case, which the student should remember, is:

$$60 \text{ m.p.h.} = 88 \text{ ft./sec.}$$

or $$1 \text{ m.p.h.} = \frac{22}{15} \text{ ft./sec.}$$

conversely, $$1 \text{ ft./sec.} = \frac{15}{22} \text{ m.p.h.}$$

85. Uniform velocity or speed.

Velocity or speed may be uniform or variable.
Uniform velocity.
A body moves with uniform velocity when throughout the motion equal distances are passed over in equal times, however small or however large.

Uniform velocity is, however, a theoretical conception. A French mathematician declared that " no conception is more simple than uniform velocity; nothing is more impossible to carry out practically ". Not only does the existence of such forces as gravity and friction make it very difficult to prevent variations, but it is practically impossible to measure either time or distance with absolute accuracy; consequently we cannot attain to absolute accuracy in experimental results.

However, the conception of uniform velocity is a very useful and important one, and is constantly employed.

The **rate of velocity** which is uniform is obtained by dividing any distance travelled by the time taken.

Thus $$\text{velocity} = \frac{\text{distance moved}}{\text{time taken}}.$$

Thus if a body moves 28 ft. in 3·5 secs

$$\text{velocity} = \frac{28 \text{ ft.}}{3\cdot5 \text{ secs.}} = 8 \text{ ft./sec.}$$

This may be generalised.

Let s = distance travelled
t = time taken
v = velocity.

Then $$v = \frac{s}{t},$$

whence $$s = vt.$$

I.e., the distance passed over is equal to the number of units of distance multiplied by the number of units of time taken for the distance.

In using the above formula, care must be taken to employ correct units.

Example. *A train running uniformly passes over half a mile in 2 mins. 12 secs. What is its velocity?*

Using $v = \dfrac{s}{t}$ and substituting given values,

$$v = \frac{\text{half a mile}}{2 \text{ min. } 12 \text{ secs.}}$$

$$= \frac{(880 \times 3) \text{ ft.}}{132 \text{ secs.}}$$

$$= 20 \text{ ft./sec.}$$

86. Average velocity.

When the velocity or speed is not uniform we can obtain the average velocity by dividing the total distance passed over by the total time taken.

If, therefore, v represents the average velocity, and s and t the total distance and time, then, as before, the formula $v = \dfrac{s}{t}$ still holds, but in the case of variable velocity v represents the average velocity for the specified distance.

This may be illustrated by a railway example.

Example.—*A train which leaves Euston at 10.50 a.m. arrives at Manchester at 3.10 p.m. What is the average velocity for the journey 210 miles?*

Time taken is 1 hr. 10 mins. + 3 hrs. 10 mins. = 4 hrs. 20 mins.

∴ Using

$$v = \frac{s}{t}, \text{ where } v = \text{average velocity,}$$

$$v = \frac{210 \text{ miles}}{4 \text{ hrs. } 20 \text{ mins.}} = \frac{210}{4\frac{1}{3}}$$

$$= 48 \cdot 4 \text{ m.p.h. nearly.}$$

87. Distance–time graphs.

The motion of a body, whether uniform or variable, can be represented graphically. The following examples illustrate the method.

(1) Uniform motion.

A motor-car passes over distances in times as shown in the following table. Exhibit them as a graph.

Time in secs. . .	1	2	3	4	5
Distances in ft. from starting point . .	20	40	60	80	100

Any of these distances divided by the corresponding interval of time gives $v = 20$ ft./sec. uniformly. Fig. 113 shows the above quantities plotted,

> time in seconds along OX.
> distances in feet ,, OY.

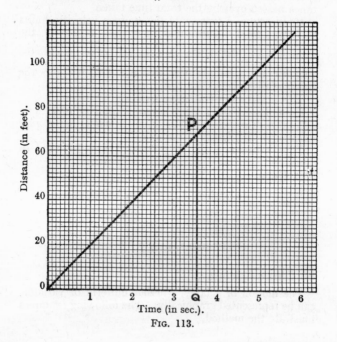

FIG. 113.

Joining the plotted points, we see that they lie on a straight line.

This is the **distance–time** graph for the motion described in the table.

If any point P be taken and PQ be drawn perpendicular to OX, the ratio $\dfrac{PQ}{OQ}$ is constant.

But $$\frac{PQ}{OQ} = \tan POQ$$
$$= \text{the gradient of } OP$$
and velocity $$= \frac{\text{distance}}{\text{time}} = \frac{PQ}{OQ}.$$

Thus the **gradient of the straight line** OP **measures the velocity.** It will be noted that when velocity is uniform the distance–time graph will always be a straight line.

(2) Velocity varying uniformly.

The following table shows the distances passed over by a falling body.

Time in secs. .	0	$\frac{1}{4}$	$\frac{1}{2}$	$\frac{3}{4}$	1	$1\frac{1}{4}$	$1\frac{1}{2}$	$1\frac{3}{4}$	2
Distance in feet	0	1	4	9	16	25	36	49	64

Representing time along OX

      ,,   distances along OY,

the values in the table are plotted as shown in Fig. 113(a).

When the points are examined they are seen to lie on a smooth curve which is part of a parabola.

The velocity thus changes from point to point.

The curve becomes steeper as the time increases. If the increases in distance over corresponding times are calculated, it will be evident that the velocity is increasing. Remembering the conclusions above, it is reasonable to conclude that if we wish to know the velocity at any particular instant, we should draw a tangent to the curve at the corresponding point. The gradient of the tangent will give the velocity at the point.

Thus to find the velocity a second after the motion has begun—*i.e.*, at the point P on the curve—a tangent to the curve should be drawn at P.

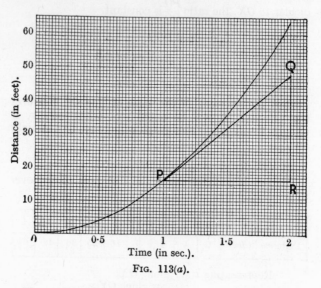

Fig. 113(*a*).

Then, completing the triangle PQR, the ratio of distance to time, *viz.* $\dfrac{QR}{PR}$ is the gradient of the curve at the point, and the gradient represents the velocity at the point.

Substituting values

$$\frac{QR}{PR} = \frac{48-16}{1} = \frac{32}{1} = 32 \text{ ft. per sec.}$$

Thus the velocity at the end of the first second is 32 ft./sec.

When a velocity is varying uniformly the graph will be a regular curve and the velocity at any point will be given by the gradient of the tangent to the curve at the point.

88. Velocity–time graphs.

Graphs which show how velocity is changing with respect to time in the motion of a body are called velocity–time graphs.

(1) The case of uniform velocity.

Let us consider the velocity–time graph for a body moving with a uniform velocity of 6 ft./secs.

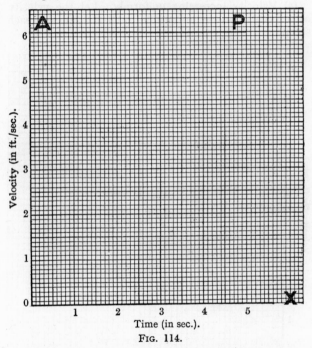

Fig. 114.

This means that no matter what the interval of time, whether it be 1 sec. or 5 secs., the velocity will be the same—*i.e.*, 6 ft./sec.

∴ The distance of any point on the graph from OX will always be the same—*i.e.*, the distance corresponding to 6 on the velocity axis.

The graph must therefore be one straight line AP, which is parallel to OX and 6 units distant from it. We may conclude :

If a body is moving with uniform velocity, its velocity–time graph will be a straight line parallel to OX.

(2) Velocity increasing or decreasing uniformly.

(*a*) **Velocity increasing uniformly.** Let the velocity of a body increase uniformly by 2 ft. per sec. each second.

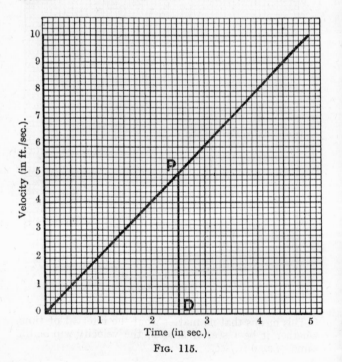

Fig. 115.

The following table shows the velocity after each second.

Time . .	0	1	2	3	4
Velocity . .	0	2	4	6	8

Fig. 115 shows the velocity–time graph of the body.

The graph is constructed by obtaining points which show the velocity at the end of each second. These points, as might be expected, lie on a straight line.

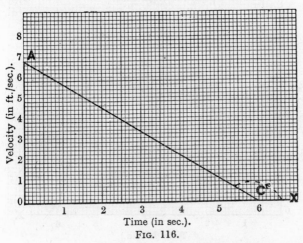

Fig. 116.

This straight line is the velocity time–graph.

If any point, P, be taken on the graph and a perpendicular PD be drawn to OX, then the ratio $\dfrac{PD}{OD}$ is constant wherever P is taken. The graph is one of constant gradient and therefore a straight line. This gradient is the tangent of the angle POD, and represents the increase in velocity per second.

(b) **Velocity decreasing uniformly.** Fig. 116 is the velocity–time graph of a body having an initial velocity of 7 ft./sec., which decreases each second by 1 ft./sec.

The decrease being uniform, the points, which mark the velocity after each second, will be found to lie on the straight line AC. The gradient of the line, as in the previous case, is given by tan ACX.

But $\angle ACX$ is an obtuse angle.

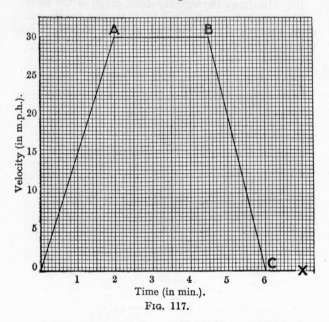

Fig. 117.

$\therefore$ tan ACX is negative.   (*Trigonometry*, § 69.)

The graph is therefore a straight line of negative gradient.

(3) Velocity–time graph of a train (velocity not uniform).

Fig. 117 represents a rough approximation of the velocity–time graph of an electric train.

The train starts from rest at O, and its velocity

increases rapidly and uniformly until in 2 mins. it reaches 30 miles an hour at A.

It then travels uniformly at 30 m.p.h. for $2\frac{1}{2}$ mins. shown at B. Afterwards its velocity decreases rapidly until the train comes to rest at C after $1\frac{1}{2}$ mins.

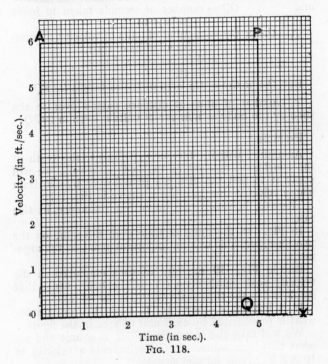

FIG. 118.

89. Area under a velocity–time graph.

Example 1.

Fig. 118, which is Fig. 114 reproduced on this page for convenience, is the velocity–time graph for a body moving for 5 secs. with a uniform velocity of 6 ft./sec. AP, parallel to OX, is the graph.

From any point P draw PQ perpendicular to OX.

The area of the rectangle $OAPQ$ is called the area under the graph.

Area of $OAPQ = OA \times OQ$.

Now $\quad\quad\quad OA$ = number of ft. per sec., *i.e.*, velocity, travelled throughout the time.

and $\quad\quad\quad OQ$ = number of seconds taken to move from A to P.

$\therefore \quad OA \times OQ$ = number of units of velocity $\times$ number of units of time,

= 6 ft. per sec. $\times$ 5 secs.

= 30 ft.

But $OA \times OQ$ = the area of the rectangle $OAPQ$.

∴ **Number of units of distance passed over in the time by the body = number of units of area in** $OAPQ$.

Example 2.

Assuming, without further experiment, the truth of the conclusion reached in the last paragraph, we will apply it to find the distance passed over by the train whose velocity–time graph was shown in Fig. 117.

There is, however, one important difference in this case.

In Fig. 118 the units of time were the same on the two axes, and this was an important point in the argument.

But in Fig. 119 the unit of time employed in the velocity scale marked on OY is the hour, while that employed in the time scale on OX is the minute.

It is important, therefore, to begin by ascertaining what is represented by each unit of area in the figure.

We will take the rectangle $OFGH$ as a unit and see what that represents. $OFGH$ represents a velocity of 10 m.p.h., acting for one *minute*.

We must therefore express the minutes in hours.

$\therefore \; OFGH$ represents 10 miles per hour for $\frac{1}{60}$ hr. = $\frac{1}{6}$ mile.

We now find the area of the whole expressed in terms of rectangle $OFGH$ as a unit.

We may either find the area of the trapezium $OABC$ by using the ordinary formula, or, by drawing AD and

BE, we can find separately the areas of the triangles *AOD*, *BEC* and the rectangle *ABED*. Regarding rectangle *OFGH* as a unit.

Area under :

$$AO = 3 \text{ units} \qquad = 3 \times \tfrac{1}{6} \text{ in.} = \tfrac{1}{2} \text{ mile.}$$
$$AB = 7\tfrac{1}{2} \text{ units} \qquad = 7\tfrac{1}{2} \times \tfrac{1}{6} \text{ ,, } = 1\tfrac{1}{4} \text{ miles.}$$
$$BC = (\tfrac{1}{2} \times 4\tfrac{1}{2}) \text{ units} = 2\tfrac{1}{4} \times \tfrac{1}{6} \text{ ,, } = \tfrac{3}{8} \text{ mile.}$$

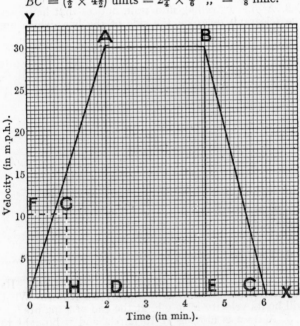

Fig. 119.

$$\therefore \text{ Total distance} = \tfrac{1}{2} + 1\tfrac{1}{4} + \tfrac{3}{8} = 2\tfrac{1}{8} \text{ miles.}$$

As was stated in § 88, the graph *OABC* is a simplified approximation to the real graph. In reality the curve would be an irregular one. The methods for finding the areas in such cases can be studied in books on " Practical " mathematics, such as *National Certificate Mathematics*.

Exercise 13

1. If a train travels 400 yds. in 12 secs., to what rate is this equivalent in :

(a) feet per second,

(b) miles per hour?

2. If a train is travelling at 24 m.p.h., how many feet will it go in 10 secs.?

3. A man travelling in a train notices that he passes the telegraph poles by the side of the line, which are 88 yds. apart, every 5 secs., on an average.

What is the train's velocity in m.p.h.?

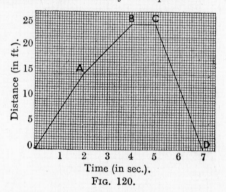

Fig. 120.

4. The speed of sound is 1100 ft. per second (approx.). What is this in miles per hour?

5. A train is moving at the rate of 14 ft./sec. Its velocity is increased each second by 0·5 ft./sec. What will be its velocity in m.p.h. at the end of a minute?

6. A train is moving at 15 m.p.h. and is brought to rest by its brakes in 10 secs. At what rate per second is its velocity decreased?

7. A train is travelling at 10 m.p.h., and its velocity is increased in each second by 3 ft./sec. Another train is moving at 15 m.p.h. and its velocity is increased by 2 ft./sec. In how many seconds will the two trains have the same velocity, and what will that be in m.p.h.?

8. Fig. 120 is the distance–time graph of a body in

motion. Find from it the average velocity from O to A, A to B, B to C, C to D.

9. The distances travelled by a moving body at intervals of 5 mins. were as shown in the following table :

Time in minutes	5	10	15	20	25	30
Distance in miles	10	15	19	22	24	25

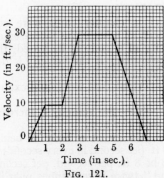

Fig. 121.

Plot the distance–time graph and find the average velocity over each of the six intervals.

10. In Fig. 121 is shown the velocity–time graph of a body moving with velocities as shown at the ends of successive seconds. Find from the graph the total distance travelled by the body.

CHAPTER IX

ACCELERATION

90. Changes in velocity.

In the previous chapter cases were considered in which the velocity of a body was increased or decreased.

If the velocity of a body is increased, the motion is said to be accelerated; if the velocity is decreased, the motion is said to be retarded.

It is very important that we should examine the **rate** at which the motion is being changed.

The rate at which the velocity is increased is called the acceleration of the body.

Thus if the velocity of a body is being uniformly increased by 3 ft. per second in every second, the acceleration is said to be 3 ft. per second, per second. The use of " per second " twice is sometimes puzzling to beginners, but a little consideration will show the need for the use of them. The first " per second " refers to the rate of the velocity and was used in this way in the previous chapter. The second " per second " gives the unit of time in which the additional amount of velocity is added on.

An acceleration of 3 ft. per second per second is usually abbreviated into 3 ft. per sec.^{2}, where the index shows that the " per sec." is repeated.

We shall make little use of the term " retardation ". The term " acceleration " is used to mean that there may be an increase or a decrease. If there is an increase the sign of the quantity is positive, if there is a decrease the sign is negative.

Thus an acceleration of -5 ft. per sec.^{2} means that the velocity is **decreasing** by 5 ft. per sec. in every second.

Other units may be used. Thus we may speak of an acceleration of 2 miles per hour per hour or 2 miles per hour.^{2}.

91. Uniform acceleration.

When the velocity of a body is increased by the same amounts in equal intervals of time, the acceleration is uniform. The cases we shall consider will be generally those of uniform acceleration.

92. Formula for a body whose motion is uniformly accelerated.

Let the velocity of a body be 10 ft. per sec.
Let it have a uniform acceleration of 3 ft. per sec.^{2}.
Then velocity after 1 sec.

$$= 10 \text{ ft. per sec.} + (1 \times 3) \text{ ft. per sec.}$$
$$= 13 \text{ ft. per sec.}$$

Velocity after 2 secs.
$= 10$ ft. per sec. $+ (2 \times 3)$ ft./sec. $= 16$ ft. per sec.
Velocity after 3 secs.
$= 10$ ft. per sec. $+ (3 \times 3)$ ft./sec. $= 19$ ft. per sec.
$\therefore$ Velocity after t secs.
$= 10$ ft. per sec. $+ (t \times 3)$ ft./sec. $= (10 + 3t)$ ft. per sec.
From inspection of these results a general formula may be readily constructed.
Let u be the initial velocity of a body in ft. per sec.
Let f be the acceleration in ft. per sec.^{2}.
Then

Velocity after 1 sec. $= (u + f)$ ft. per sec.
„   „   2 secs. $= (u + 2f)$ ft. per sec.
„   „   3 secs. $= (u + 3f)$ ft. per sec.

And generally

Velocity after t secs. $= \{u + (t \times f)\}$ ft. per sec.

Let v be the velocity after t secs.
Then $v = (u + ft.)$ ft. per sec.
The same formula will be true whatever the units

employed, provided they are the same throughout. Therefore we may state the formula generally as :

$$v = u + ft.$$

from which $$t = \frac{v - u}{f}.$$

Also $$f = \frac{v - u}{t}.$$

93. Average velocity and distance.

Fig. 122 represents the general velocity time diagram of a body, with uniform acceleration.

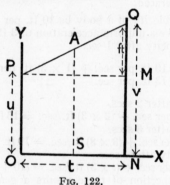

FIG. 122.

Let
- u = initial velocity.
- v = final velocity.
- f = acceleration.
- t = time.

In the figure

OP represents u
QN „ v
ON „ t

Draw PM parallel to OX.
Then QM represents $f \times t$, increase in velocity.

Also $$QN = MN + QM.$$
$$= OP + QM.$$
or $$v = u + ft.$$

Let A be the mid point of PQ.

Draw AS perpendicular to ON.

Now, as shown in the previous chapter :

Distance passed over by the moving body is represented by the area under the graph.

∴ Distance passed over in the above case is represented by the area of the trapezium $OPQN$.

Using the formula for the area of a trapezium :

Area of $OPQN = \frac{1}{2}(OP + NQ) \times ON$
$$= \frac{1}{2}(u + v) \times t.$$

∴ If s = distance passed over

$$S = \frac{u + v}{2} \times t.$$

Also, we know from Geometry that

$$AS = \frac{1}{2}(OP + QN)$$
$$= \frac{1}{2}(u + v).$$

∴ Average of initial and final velocities

= velocity at the middle of the interval.

∴ S = (average of initial and final velocities) × t.

Also S = (velocity at the middle of the interval) × t.

94. Distance passed over by a uniformly accelerated body.

Let u, v, t, s represent the same quantities as in the previous paragraph.

As shown above,

$$\frac{u + v}{2} = \text{average velocity} \qquad . \quad . \quad (1)$$

$$s = \frac{u + v}{2} \times t \quad . \quad . \quad . \quad . \quad (2)$$

and $\qquad v = u + ft \quad . \quad . \quad . \quad . \quad . \quad (3)$

In (2) for v substitute $u + ft$ from (3).

Then $\qquad s = \frac{u + (u + ft)}{2} \times t.$

$$= \frac{2u + ft}{2} \times t.$$

∴ $\qquad s = ut + \frac{1}{2}ft^2.$

Again from (2)

$$s = \frac{u + v}{2} \times t.$$

$$\therefore \qquad u + v = \frac{2s}{t}.$$

Also $\qquad v - u = ft.$

Multiplying $\qquad v^2 - u^2 = 2fs.$

Whence $\qquad s = \frac{v^2 - u^2}{2f}.$

This gives a formula for the distance in terms of the initial and final velocities.

Collecting the formulæ

(1) $\boldsymbol{v = u + ft.}$

(2) $\boldsymbol{s = \left(\dfrac{u + v}{2}\right) \times t.}$

(3) $\boldsymbol{s = ut + \frac{1}{2}ft^2.}$

(4) $\boldsymbol{v^2 - u^2 = 2fs.}$

If a body starts from rest, then $u = 0$ and we get :

(5) $\boldsymbol{v = ft.}$

(6) $\boldsymbol{s = \frac{1}{2}ft^2.}$

(7) $\boldsymbol{v^2 = 2fs.}$

95. Retardation.

When a body is uniformly retarded, f is replaced by $-f$, and the formulæ above which contain f become :

$$v = u - ft.$$
$$s = ut - \tfrac{1}{2}ft^2.$$
$$v^2 = u^2 - 2fs.$$

96. Worked examples.

Example 1. *A train moving at 20 m.p.h. is uniformly accelerated so that after 8 secs. its velocity is 30 m.p.h. Find the acceleration in ft./sec.² and the distance the train goes in the interval.*

Here $\qquad u = 20$ m.p.h.

$$= 20 \times \frac{22}{15} \text{ ft./sec.}$$

$$= \frac{88}{3} \text{ ft./sec.}$$

and
$$v = 30 \text{ m.p.h.}$$
$$= 30 \times \frac{22}{15} \text{ ft./sec.}$$
$$= 44 \text{ ft./sec.}$$

To find acceleration.

Using
$$v = u + ft.$$

Then
$$44 = \frac{88}{3} + 8f.$$

$$\therefore \qquad 8f = 44 - \frac{88}{3} = \frac{44}{3}.$$

$$\therefore \qquad f = \frac{11}{6} \text{ ft. per sec.}^2.$$

To find distance.

Using
$$s = ut + \tfrac{1}{2}ft^2.$$
$$s = \left(\frac{88}{3} \times 8\right) + \frac{1}{2} \cdot \frac{11}{6} \cdot (8)^2.$$
$$= \frac{8 \times 88}{3} + \frac{2 \times 88}{3} = \frac{10 \times 88}{3}.$$

$$\therefore \qquad s = 293\tfrac{1}{3} \text{ ft.}$$

It should be noted that s can also be found from the formula $2fs = v^2 - u^2$. This could be done as a check.

Example 2.—*A body has an initial velocity of 15 m.p.h. and is uniformly accelerated at the rate of 1 yd./sec.² for $\frac{1}{4}$ mile. Find in feet per second the velocity it acquires.*

$$15 \text{ m.p.h.} = 15 \times \frac{22}{15} \text{ ft./sec.}$$
$$= 22 \text{ ft./sec.}$$

Acceleration
$$= 1 \text{ yd./sec.}^2.$$
$$= 3 \text{ ft./sec.}^2,$$

and
$$s = 1320.$$

To find final velocity.

Using
$$v^2 - u^2 = 2fs$$
$$v^2 = u^2 + 2fs$$
$$= 22^2 + (2 \times 3 \times 1320)$$
$$= 8404$$

$$\therefore \qquad v = \sqrt{8404}$$
$$= 91 \cdot 7 \text{ ft./sec.}$$

Example 3.—*The brakes on a train reduce its speed from 60 to 20 m.p.h. while it runs 220 yds. Assuming that they exert a constant retarding force, find how much farther the train will run before coming to rest and how long it will take.*

$$60 \text{ m.p.h.} = 60 \times \frac{22}{15} = 88 \text{ ft./sec.}$$

$$20 \text{ m.p.h.} = \frac{88}{3} \text{ ft./sec.}$$

The decrease in velocity takes place in 660 ft.

∴ To find the retardation :

Use $$2fs = v^2 - u^2.$$

∴ $$2 \times 660 \times f = 88^2 - \left(\frac{88}{3}\right)^2,$$

whence $$f = \frac{704}{135} \text{ ft./sec.}^2.$$

To find the distance before stopping, remembering the final velocity is zero, we use

$$v = ft.$$

∴ $$t = \frac{v}{f}$$

$$= \frac{88}{3} \div \frac{704}{135}.$$

Whence $$t = 5\tfrac{5}{8} \text{ secs.}$$

To find the distance travelled, use :

$$s = \tfrac{1}{2}ft^2. \qquad (See \ \S \ 94.)$$

Substituting $$s = \frac{1}{2} \times \frac{704}{135} \times \left(\frac{45}{8}\right)^2,$$

whence $$s = 82 \cdot 5 \text{ ft.}$$

Exercise 14

1. A body starts from rest and moves with an acceleration of 5 ft./sec.² What will be its velocity after 8 secs., and how far will it have gone?

2. How long would a body moving under the conditions of the previous question take to travel a quarter of a mile?

3. A train is moving at 30 m.p.h. If brakes are put

on and the train is retarded at the rate of 2 ft./sec.^{2}, when will it come to rest, and how far will it travel in doing so?

4. A train starting from a station reaches a velocity of 30 m.p.h. in 40 secs. Find the acceleration and the distance travelled by the train in 40 secs.

5. A train travelling at 48 m.p.h. is brought to rest by its brakes in 22 secs. What is its retardation in ft./sec.^{2}, and how far does it travel in the time?

6. The velocity of a motor-car is increased from 10 m.p.h. to 30 m.p.h. in travelling 220 ft. What was the acceleration of the car, and how long did it take to travel the distance?

7. The velocity of a train was increased from rest by 2 ft./sec.^{2} for 24 secs. It was then retarded at 1·5 ft./sec.^{2} until it came to rest. How far did it travel in all?

8. A body starting from rest has a constant acceleration of 4 ft./sec.^{2}. How far will it travel in the 10th sec.?

9. A train is moving at 36 m.p.h. If it is to pull up in 160 yds., what must be the retardation?

10. A car travelling at 40 m.p.h. has its velocity reduced in 2·5 secs. to 10 m.p.h. What distance was covered in the time?

11. A train moves from rest with a uniform acceleration of 1·5 ft./sec.^{2}. After what time and distance will its velocity be 30 m.p.h.?

12. A slip carriage is detached from a train moving at 60 m.p.h. If it comes to rest in 1100 yds., how long is this after it leaves the train?

13. A body has an initial velocity of 15 ft./sec. and an acceleration of 12 ft./sec.^{2}. How long will it take to travel 750 ft.?

14. The brakes on a train reduce its speed from 60 to 20 m.p.h. while it runs 220 yds. Assuming that they exert a constant retarding force, find how much farther the train will run before coming to rest and how long it will take.

97. Acceleration due to gravity.

The most common example which we experience of accelerated velocity is that of gravity. It had been observed in the earliest days of the human race that if a body fell from a height to the ground, the farther it fell, the greater was its velocity on reaching the ground. Speculation about it, however, was mainly concerned with the question : Why does the body fall? To this problem the answer has not yet been found. The great mathematician, Galileo, seems to have been the first to consider the question : *How* does it fall? That is, what is the nature of the motion itself? Is it uniformly accelerated? What is the acceleration? These are the kind of questions that Galileo set himself to answer. He left for future generations the problem of the cause of the motion.

Before the time of Galileo it had been generally accepted that a heavy body fell to the ground with greater velocity than a light body. This was superficially deduced from the fact that such an object as a feather would flutter slowly to the ground, whereas a piece of stone falls rapidly.

Galileo, however, performed the experiment of dropping bodies of different weights from the top of the leaning tower of Pisa, and showed that they reached the ground in approximately the same time. But his experiments and deductions did not convince the doubters and he was expelled from the University of Pisa.

In the next century Sir Isaac Newton showed that the resistance of the air accounted for the differences in the times that certain bodies took in falling by performing his famous experiment of dropping a feather and a guinea in a cylindrical glass vessel from which nearly all the air had been exhausted. He showed that both feather and coin fell in the same time.

98. The acceleration of a falling body.

Since the time of Galileo various forms of apparatus have been devised to show that bodies fall with uniform acceleration and to discover what is the amount of the acceleration. The student who has access to a physical laboratory will be able to study these experiments, but in this book we must be content with stating what are the facts which they demonstrate. By means of them we learn that—

The acceleration of a falling body is uniform and is approximately 32 ft. per sec.^{2}.

The letter g is always used to denote this acceleration.

The value of g is given above as approximately 32 ft. per sec.^{2}, but it varies slightly at different places on the earth's surface, for reasons which will not be considered now. It has its greatest value at the poles, where it is approximately equal to 32·25, and its least value at the equator, where it is 32·09, the figure again approximate.

At Greenwich the value of g in vacuo, *i.e.*, the air resistance eliminated, is 32·19078 ft./sec.^{2}, correct to five places of decimals: generally, in this book we shall follow the custom of assuming the value of 32 ft./sec.^{2}.

The corresponding value to this in the metric system is 980 cm./sec.^{2}.

99. Formulae for motion under gravity.

The formulæ proved in § 94 were general and hold for any uniform acceleration. They are therefore true for falling bodies, but it is usual, when employing them, to replace f by g. With this substitution the formulæ are as follows :—

$$(1) \quad v = u + gt.$$
$$(2) \quad s = \left(\frac{u + v}{2}\right) \times t.$$
$$(3) \quad s = ut + \tfrac{1}{2}gt^2.$$
$$(4) \quad v^2 - u^2 = 2gh.$$

If a body is dropped from a height, it starts with zero velocity, and consequently the formulæ are modified as follows :

$$(5) \quad v = gt.$$
$$(6) \quad s = \tfrac{1}{2}gt^2.$$
$$(7) \quad v^2 = 2gh.$$

If g be taken as equal to 32, then (5) and (6) become :

$$v = 32t.$$
$$s = 16t^2.$$

These are useful forms to remember.

100. Motion of a body projected vertically upwards.

When a body is projected upwards, the motion is retarded, *i.e.*, the acceleration is negative. It will rise until it reaches its maximum height, when for an instant the velocity is zero. If v is the velocity of projection, then time to reach this is given by

$$t = \frac{v}{g}.$$

If h be the greatest height, then, using formula 7 above,

$$h = \frac{v^2}{2g}.$$

At the maximum height the motion of the body is reversed and the body begins to fall under the action of gravity, *i.e.*, with acceleration g.

Consequently if there were no air resistance, it would reach the ground again in the time it took to rise and with the velocity with which it was projected, but in the opposite direction.

The circumstances of the downward path are those of the upward reversed.

The total time from ground to ground will be

$$2t \text{ or } \frac{2v}{g}.$$

The total distance will be

$$2h \text{ or } \frac{v^2}{g}.$$

101. Worked example.

A bullet is shot vertically upwards with a velocity of 160 ft./sec. from a stationary balloon, 320 ft. above the ground. Find :

(1) *The greatest height and the time taken to reach it.*

(2) *Time to reach the ground, assuming no interception by the balloon.*

(3) *The velocity on reaching the ground.*

(Air resistance is to be ignored throughout.)

(1) Time and greatest height.
Using the formula
$$t = \frac{v}{g}.$$
$$t = \frac{160}{32} = 5 \text{ secs.}$$

Height.
Using $\quad s = 16t^2$
we have $\quad s = 16 \times 5^2 = 400$ ft. (above the balloon).

(2) From the greatest height the bullet has to fall, *viz.*

(dist. above the balloon) + (dist. of balloon above ground)
$$= 400 \text{ ft.} + 320 \text{ ft.} = 720 \text{ ft.}$$
Using $\quad s = \frac{1}{2}gt^2, \quad 720 = 16t^2$
$$t^2 = 45$$
$$t = \sqrt{45} = 6 \cdot 7 \text{ secs. (approx.).}$$

This is the time from the highest point, but it took 5 secs. to rise to that.
$$\therefore \text{ Total time } = 6 \cdot 7 + 5 = 11 \cdot 7 \text{ secs.}$$

(3) Velocity on reaching the ground.

Using $\quad v^2 = 2gh$
we have $\quad v^2 = 2 \times 64 \times 720$
$$v = 32 \times \sqrt{45} = 214 \text{ ft./sec. (approx.).}$$

(Or the formula $v = gt$ could be used.)

Exercise 15.

Note.—In the following questions air resistance is neglected. Take $g = 32$.

1. In the following table fill in the velocities and distance passed over by a body falling from rest.

Time (secs.) .	0	$\frac{1}{2}$	1	$1\frac{1}{2}$	2	$2\frac{1}{2}$
Velocity (ft./sec.)	0					
Distance . .	0					

From these results draw :

    (1) A time–distance graph ;
    (2) A velocity–time graph.

Use the method of the area under the graph to find the distance passed over in 2 secs.

2. A stone is dropped from the top of a building and reaches the ground after $2\frac{1}{4}$ secs. How high is the building ?

3. How long does it take a falling body to acquire a velocity of 100 ft./sec., and through what distance does it fall in the time ?

4. A body is projected vertically upwards with a velocity of 160 ft./sec. Find the greatest height it will reach and the time taken.

5. A stone is thrown vertically upwards and returns to the ground after 5 secs. Find its initial velocity and the greatest height reached.

6. What is the velocity of a body after it has fallen 100 ft., and how long does it take ?

7. A stone is dropped from a stationary balloon. How far does it fall in the 4th second ?

8. A stone is projected vertically upwards with a velocity of 80 ft./sec. After what times is it 84 ft. above the ground ?

9. A balloon is rising vertically with a velocity of 40 ft./sec. A stone is dropped from it and reaches the ground in 3 secs. How high is the balloon ?

10. A body is projected vertically upwards with a velocity of 80 ft./sec. What is its velocity when it has risen 64 ft. ? How long will this be after the moment of projection ?

11. A balloon ascends from rest with uniform acceleration, and a stone is dropped from it after 6 secs. The stone reaches the ground 4 secs. after being released. Find the acceleration of the balloon and the height from which the stone fell.

12. Find the greatest height attained by a projectile which is thrown vertically upwards with a velocity of 25 metres per sec., and also the time which elapses before it returns to its point of departure ($g = 980$ cm./sec.^{2}).

CHAPTER X

NEWTON'S LAWS OF MOTION

102. Mass and acceleration.

In the previous chapter the formulæ relating to accelerated motion were investigated, but without any reference to the mass of the moving body. We must now examine the connection between mass and motion and consider the laws which lie at the foundation of changes in velocity.

103. Mass and weight.

At the outset it is essential that the student should be quite clear in his mind as to the distinction between mass and weight, two terms which are frequently confused. There was a brief reference to these in Chapter I, and they have frequently been employed in subsequent chapters. The following definitions will serve to remind the student of the fundamental differences between mass and weight.

Weight is a force.

It is the attractive force called gravitation, by which, unless prevented by some other force, bodies will move vertically downwards towards the earth with uniform acceleration.

Mass is the quantity of matter in a body.

The weight of a body varies at different parts of the earth's surface (see § 98).

The mass of a body remains constant as the body is moved from place to place. It is constant whatever the velocity with which the body moves. If we were to conceive the attraction of the earth to be eliminated, the mass of the body would remain unaltered but there would be no weight.

104. Measurement of mass.

Standard unit of mass. We need to measure mass, and for purposes of comparison a standard unit of mass is preserved in London. It is a mass of one pound of platinum.

Comparison of mass. Masses can be compared as to the amount of matter in them by the action of force upon them.

Equal masses are such that if acted upon by equal forces equal accelerations are produced.

The *attraction of the earth,* i.e., *the force of gravity,* is the best available force for the purpose of comparison.

This attraction measures the weight of the mass, and when the attraction on a mass is equal to the attraction on the *standard unit of mass, its weight is one pound.*

Weight, then, is employed to measure mass, and **the weight of a body is the measure of its mass.**

Weight is therefore proportional to mass.

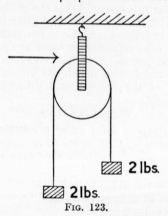

Fig. 123.

105. Mass and inertia.

Let two masses of, say, 2 lbs. each be suspended by a fine string which passes over a smooth pulley (Fig. 123). The bodies will rest in equilibrium in any position.

To set them in motion force is necessary.

Let a tangential force be applied at the top of pulley in a direction shown by the arrow. The two weights will move. If greater weights were employed, greater force would be necessary to produce motion.

Similarly if a large steel fly-wheel mounted on a smooth axle were at rest, force would be necessary to move it round.

Now, it will be noticed that the force employed is not required to overcome the force of gravity, since whether it be the arrangement of weights described above or a large fly-wheel, the weight on one side is balanced by that on the other. By using a perfectly smooth pulley and a smooth axle, the action of friction is almost negligible, or not sufficient to account for the effort required.

We have also seen in Chapter VII that if a body has been set in motion by a force, and that force no longer acts, the motion tends to continue. For example, if a heavy, smooth steel ball be propelled across smooth ice, it tends to continue in motion for a long time, and force must be applied to stop it. The weight of the ball is borne by the ice, and has no horizontal component which affects the motion.

Again, if a heavy ship is moving with high velocity and the engines are stopped, it is a considerable time before it comes to rest owing to water and air resistance.

From the consideration of phenomena such as have been described above, we come to the conclusion that there is inherent in mass a property, not weight, which apparently offers resistance to attempts to impart motion or to change of motion.

This property of mass is called inertia.

106. Newton's Laws of Motion.

The above principle of inertia is inherent in the first of Newton's Laws of Motion.

Newton's First Law of Motion.

Every body continues in its state of rest or of uniform motion in a straight line except when it is compelled by external force to change that state.

F—MECH.

This law does two things :

    (1) It is an expression of the **property of inertia** in matter.

    (2) In effect it defines **a force as that which changes the state of rest or the motion of a body.**

The law explains a principle of great importance to traffic engineers. Suppose a locomotive increases its speed until it reaches the highest speed at which it is desired to run a train—say, 40 m.p.h. Assuming the truth of the above law, if steam were now shut off, the train would continue to move uniformly at 40 m.p.h., unless compelled to change that speed by external force.

Friction and air resistances are the only external forces which would thus act on the train, provided it is travelling on perfectly horizontal rails. Consequently it is necessary for the steam to provide only sufficient force to overcome these resistances, and a comparatively small force is required to effect this.

107. Newton's Laws and dynamics.

The above law is the first of three, and the investigation of the remaining two will follow. They were first formally expressed by Sir Isaac Newton in the seventeenth century.

They are the fundamental laws upon which the whole science of dynamics is built up.

The laws are axiomatic—that is, they are not capable of mathematical proof, though experiments may be devised which provide corroboration of their truth. Perhaps the most striking verification of them is found in astronomical predictions. For the assumption that the laws are true enables mathematical investigators to publish in advance, in the *Nautical Almanac*, predictions of the movements and positions of the sun, moon, planets and other heavenly bodies. They predict eclipses, forecast the times of tides, the daily times of sunset and sunrise. The accuracy of these and hundreds of other phenomena, dependent on the fundamental Laws of Motion, is never questioned, and they are never found to be incorrect.

108. Newton's Second Law of Motion.

The first law defines force; the second deals with its measurement. It is as follows :

Newton's Second Law of Motion.

The rate of change of motion is proportional to applied force and takes place in the direction in which the force acts.

Whatever the nature of the force it must be measured by the results observed in the body moved. Clearly, then, we must have regard not only to the change in velocity, but also to the mass which is moved. For the same force acting on a locomotive and on a wheelbarrow would produce very different velocities, because of their different masses. Again, the force which would bring a rowing-boat to rest would have very little effect upon a liner.

109. Momentum.

Therefore the effect of a force in changing the motion of a body, or bringing it to rest, must depend on two things :

(1) The **mass** of the body.
(2) The **velocity** of the body.

Consequently when it is stated in the Second Law that " the rate of change of motion is proportional to the impressed force ", the term " change of motion " must mean more than change of velocity, since for a given force the change of velocity must depend on the " mass " moving or to be moved. Therefore by " motion " we must understand what is called **" momentum ",** which is the product of the mass of a body and its velocity.

Let m represents the mass of a body
and v „ its velocity,

Let the unit of momentum be taken as a unit of mass moving with unit of velocity.

Then **momentum is represented by** *mv.*

Thus a mass of 10 lbs. moving with a velocity of 2 ft./sec. would have $10 \times 2 = 20$ units of momentum, and a mass of 2 lbs. moving with a velocity of 10 ft./sec. would have $2 \times 10 = 20$ units of momentum.

110. The Second Law of Motion can therefore be written in the following form:

The rate of change of momentum is proportional to the applied force, and takes place in the direction in which the applied force acts.

If the mass of a body be constant, the rate of change of momentum implies the rate of change of velocity— *i.e.*, acceleration.

Consequently we may deduce that the acceleration produced in the body is proportional to the applied force. Conversely a force is proportional to the acceleration it produces in a given mass.

Equal masses. It also follows that bodies in which the same force produces the same acceleration must have equal masses.

These important principles can be confirmed by experiments with suitable apparatus, such as Fletcher's Trolley. These can be observed in a laboratory; to describe them here would not convey much to the student.

111. Equation connecting force and acceleration.

We can now proceed to obtain the very important formula which connects force and the acceleration produced in a body on which it acts.

Let m = the mass of a body.

  ,, P = the force acting on it.

  ,, f = the acceleration produced.

Then, as has been shown above,

$$P \text{ is proportional to } mf.$$

$$\therefore \quad P = kmf$$

where k is a constant.

The value of k will depend on the units which are adopted for the quantities P, m, and f.

Two alternative forms may be adopted:

(1) Gravitational unit of force.

Let the unit of mass be 1 lb.

"   "   force be the weight of 1 lb.

Now, if a body of weight 1 lb. falls and is acted upon by gravity, its acceleration is g.

∴ A force of 1 lb. wt., acting on a mass of 1 lb. produces an acceleration represented by g.

∴ In the equation :

$$P = kmf. \quad \ldots \quad \ldots \quad (A)$$

If $P = 1$, and $m = 1$, then $f = g = 32$ (approx.). Substituting $\quad 1 = k \times 1 \times g$.

∴ $$k = \frac{1}{g}.$$

∴ The equation becomes :

$$P = \frac{mf}{g},$$

or $$\frac{P}{m} = \frac{f}{g} \quad \ldots \quad \ldots \quad (1)$$

In this form, it must be emphasised that—

the unit of force is the weight of 1 lb.
the unit of mass is a mass of 1 lb.

(2) Absolute unit of force.

Let the unit of mass be 1 lb.

"   "   acceleration be 1 ft./sec.^{2}.

Now, if the unit of force be chosen so that $k = 1$. Then, when $m = 1$ and $f = 1$, $P = 1$.

∴ Substituting in equation (A) :

$$P = mf.$$

The unit of force now is that force which, acting on a mass of 1 lb., produces an acceleration of 1 ft./sec.^{2}.

But a force of 1 lb. weight acting on a mass of 1 lb. produces an acceleration of g (32) ft./sec.^{2}.

∴ When the equation is in the form

$$P = mf$$

the unit of force must be $\frac{1}{g}$ or $\frac{1}{32}$ of a lb.—*i.e.*, the weight of about half an ounce.

This unit of force is called the poundal.

∴ If the formula is in the form

$$P = mf$$

P is in poundals, m in lbs. mass.

The previous paragraph is of very great importance, and the student should study it several times and master it before proceeding further.

(3) The two forms compared.

The first method—the gravitational unit of force—is used by engineers. For example, the pull of a locomotive is measured in pounds, or in tons for large forces; pressures are measured in lbs. per sq. in.; many similar instances could be given.

The disadvantage of working with such a unit is that it is not a fixed quantity; its value depends on g and, as we have seen, this differs very slightly in various parts of the earth's surface.

On the other hand, the poundal has a fixed value, since it is that force which produces in a unit of mass an acceleration of 1 ft./sec.^{2}. It is independent of g. Consequently the **poundal is called the absolute unit of force.**

For the purpose of solving problems, the student will probably find that the first method is the better, and this is best remembered in the form

$$\frac{P}{m} = \frac{f}{g}.$$

In centimetre gram second (C.G.S.) units the absolute unit of force is that which produces an acceleration of 1 cm. per sec. in a mass of 1 gram.

This unit is called a dyne.

112. Worked examples.

Owing to the importance of the foregoing, a larger number of examples than usual are worked out for the consideration of the student.

Example 1. *A force of 6 lbs. wt. acts on a mass of 15 lbs. What acceleration is produced in the mass?*

Using the gravitational unit of force and the formulae

$$\frac{P}{m} = \frac{f}{g}$$

we have $\qquad P = 6, m = 15, g = 32.$

Substituting these values,

$$\frac{6}{15} = \frac{f}{32},$$

Whence $\qquad f = \frac{6 \times 32}{15} = 12 \cdot 8 \text{ ft./sec.}^2.$

Example 2. *What is the force which, acting on a body whose weight is 10 lbs., produces an acceleration of 8 ft./sec.²?*

Using $\qquad\qquad \frac{P}{m} = \frac{f}{g},$

and substituting the given values we get :

$$\frac{P}{10} = \frac{8}{32}.$$

$\therefore \qquad\qquad P = \frac{8 \times 10}{32} = 2 \cdot 5 \text{ lbs. wt.}$

Example 3. *A force of 6 lbs. wt. acts on a mass of 10 lbs. for 4 secs. What velocity does it acquire, and how far does it travel in the 4 secs.?*

We must first find the acceleration which the body receives.

Using $\qquad\qquad \frac{P}{m} = \frac{f}{g},$

on substitution

$$\frac{6}{10} = \frac{f}{32}.$$

$\therefore \qquad\qquad 10f = 192$

and $\qquad\qquad f = 19 \cdot 2 \text{ ft./sec.}^2.$

Therefore the body starts from rest with an acceleration of 19·2 ft./sec.^{2}.

(1) **To find the velocity acquired in 4 secs.**

Using $v = ft$

on substitution

$$v = 19·2 \times 4 = 76·8 \text{ ft./sec.}$$

(2) **To find the distance travelled.**

Using $\quad s = \frac{1}{2}ft^2$

$$s = \frac{1}{2} \times 19·2 \times 4^2$$
$$= 153·6 \text{ ft.}$$

Example 4. *A train whose weight is 420 tons reaches a speed of 30 m.p.h. in 30 secs. after starting from rest. What force does the engine exert on the train?*

We must first find the acceleration of the train. It is such that the velocity after 30 secs. is 30 m.p.h.

Now $\quad$ 30 m.p.h. $= 30 \times \dfrac{22}{15} = 44$ ft./sec.

Using $\qquad f = \dfrac{v}{t}$

to find the acceleration f, we have

$$f = \frac{44}{30} \text{ ft./sec.}^2.$$

Having found the acceleration produced, to find the force producing it we use

$$\frac{P}{m} = \frac{f}{g}.$$

Substituting the values for m, f, g,

$$\frac{P}{420} = \frac{\frac{44}{30}}{32}.$$

[*Note.*—On the left-hand side, both P and m can be expressed in tons; the ratio is the same as if they were expressed in lbs.]

From this equation

$$P = \frac{420 \times 44}{30 \times 32} = \frac{77}{4}.$$

∴ $\qquad P = 19\frac{1}{4}$ tons wt.

Example 5. *A motor-car weighing 16 cwt. is moving at 30 m.p.h. It is brought to rest by the brakes in 66 ft. What was the force applied by the brakes?*

$$30 \text{ m.p.h.} = 30 \times \frac{22}{15} = 44 \text{ ft./sec.}$$

To find the acceleration knowing the distance, we use the formula

$$v^2 = 2fs$$

or

$$f = \frac{v^2}{2s}.$$

Substituting

$$f = \frac{44^2}{2 \times 66} = \frac{44}{3} \text{ ft./sec.}^2.$$

To find the force of the brakes we use

$$\frac{P}{m} = \frac{f}{g}.$$

Substituting

$$\frac{P}{16} = \frac{\frac{44}{3}}{32}.$$

∴

$$P = \frac{44 \times 16}{3 \times 32} = 7\tfrac{1}{3} \text{ cwt. wt.}$$

Example 6. *A lift is ascending with an acceleration of 2 ft./sec.². A man holds a spring-balance from which a parcel weighing 3 lbs. is hung. What is the reading of the spring-balance?*

Fig. 124 shows the forces acting on the parcel. These are:

(1) Weight, 3 lbs. downwards.
(2) Upward pull of spring balance.

Let this be T.

T is registered on the spring-balance.

The Resultant force acting on parcel is $T - 3$ upwards.

The mass acted on is 3 lbs.

The acceleration is 2 ft./sec.².

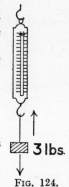

Fig. 124.

Using
$$\frac{P}{m} = \frac{f}{g},$$

and substituting known values :

$$\frac{T-3}{3} = \frac{2}{32}.$$

$$\therefore \quad T-3 = \frac{3}{16}.$$
$$T = 3 + \frac{3}{16}$$
$$= 3 \text{ lbs. 3 ozs.}$$

Note.—If the lift were going down with an acceleration, the resultant force acting on the parcel would be $3 - T$.

Example 7. *A truck weighing 2 tons is to be hauled up an incline of 1 in 12. What constant force, applied parallel to the plane, is required to move it with a constant acceleration of 4 in./sec.²?*

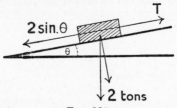

2 sin θ

T

θ

↓ 2 tons

Fig. 125.

Let T in tons wt. be the force acting parallel to and up the plane.

Resolved part of weight acting down the plane
$$= 2 \sin \theta \quad . \quad . \quad . \quad . \quad . \quad (\S 56)$$
$$= 2 \times \tfrac{1}{12} = \tfrac{1}{6} \text{ ton wt.}$$

∴ **Resultant force** acting up the plane $= (T - \tfrac{1}{6})$ tons wt.

This acts on a mass of 2 tons.

∴ Using
$$\frac{P}{m} = \frac{f}{g},$$
$$\frac{T - \tfrac{1}{6}}{2} = \frac{\tfrac{4}{12}}{32} = \tfrac{1}{96}.$$

$$\therefore \quad T - \tfrac{1}{6} = \tfrac{1}{48}.$$
$$T = \tfrac{1}{6} + \tfrac{1}{48}.$$
$$= \tfrac{3}{16} \text{ ton wt.}$$

Exercise 16

1. A mass of 10 lbs. is acted on by a force of 4 lbs. weight. What is the acceleration which is produced?

2. What force acting on a mass of 16 lbs. will produce an acceleration of 6 ft./sec.²?

3. A force of 10 lbs. weight acting on a body produces an acceleration of 5 ft./sec.². What is the weight of the body?

4. The velocity of a motor-car weighing a ton increases from rest to 24 m.p.h. in 8 secs. What was the force acting on it in cwt., assuming this to be constant throughout the time?

5. An engine exerts a pull of $7\frac{1}{2}$ tons wt. on a train whose weight, with the engine, is 200 tons. The resistances to motion amount to 2 tons weight. Find the acceleration of the train in ft./sec.².

6. If a car weighing 3000 lbs. and travelling at 25 m.p.h. is brought to rest in 20 yds., what is the average force acting?

7. A body of mass 10 lbs. acted on by a constant force for 1 min. acquires thereby a velocity of 1000 yds. per min. Determine the value of the force.

8. A train weighing 210 tons and running at 25 m.p.h. has its velocity reduced to 10 m.p.h. in 12 secs. What was the force, in lbs. wt., which retarded it?

9. A shell weighing 16 lbs. falls for 3 secs. and penetrates a sand-heap to a depth of 1 ft. Find the average resistance of the sand.

10. A motor-car travelling at 30 m.p.h. is brought to rest in 30 yds. What is the average force in tons wt. which is applied to the car if its mass is 1 ton?

11. A man in a lift holds a spring-balance, with a 7-lb. weight hanging from it. The lift descends, (a) with downward acceleration 4 ft./sec.²; (b) with a uniform speed of 6 ft./sec.²; (c) with an upward acceleration of 2 ft./sec.². What should be the readings of the spring balance in each case?

12. A weight of 6 lbs. is lowered by a string, and the acceleration of the weight is 2 ft./sec.². What is the tension in the string?

13. In launching a ship of 5000 tons it is necessary to

stop her in 500 ft. after leaving the slip. If she leaves the slip with a velocity of 8 ft./sec., what will be the average force of retardation which will bring her to rest within the distance?

14. A man of weight 12 stone is in a lift which is moving upwards with an acceleration of 5 ft./sec.^{2}. What is his pressure on the floor of the lift?

15. A trolley weighing 200 lbs. is pulled up a smooth incline of 1 in 10 with an acceleration of 2 ft./sec.^{2}. What is the force acting parallel to the incline?

113. Newton's Third Law of Motion.

To every action there is an equal and opposite reaction.

The student has become acquainted with this law in a statical form. For example, when a body rests in equilibrium on a horizontal table it has been reasoned that the table must exert an upward pressure on the body equal and opposite to the weight of the body acting downward. Since there is no other force acting on the body—its weight has no horizontal component—if there is equilibrium these forces must be equal and opposite.

Although the student, from examples such as this, is prepared to accept the law in its statical form, it does not seem so obvious when applied to bodies in motion. It is, however, universally applicable.

114. Dynamical aspect of the Third Law.

If there is pressure, there must be counter-pressure. When a board is hanging in air suspended by a couple of cords, we know it would be impossible to drive a nail into it. If we want to do this the board must be so supported as to offer resistance to the passage of the nail. It must be possible for a resistance to be offered by the board, which is equal and opposite to the pressure of the nail on the board.

At first sight it may appear to the student that the existence of two equal and opposite forces would produce equilibrium, as in the case of the table mentioned in § 113, and that there would be no motion. To explain the apparent anomaly we cannot do better than use the illustration which Newton himself employed—that of a horse drawing a cart.

In Fig. 126 is a representation of this. The force exerted by the horse acts along the trace.

We will assume for simplicity that the motion of the horse and cart is horizontal. We have, then, to deal only with horizontal forces. All of these must be carefully examined and stated.

Let T be the tension along the trace.

Then by the Third Law, the force T acting on the cart gives rise to an equal and opposite force T, which acts on the horse.

FIG. 126.

The question then is "How can the horse and cart move at all?" The answer is twofold:

(1) **The two forces act on different bodies,** one on the cart, one on the horse.

(2) **There are other forces acting** on the horse and cart separately. Of these we need not consider vertical forces, since they have no horizontal components.

First, let us consider the horse.

As the horse presses the ground with his feet there is, in accordance with the Third Law, an equal and opposite reaction of the ground upon the horse.

Let P be the horizontal component of this.

Now P acts in a forward direction.

∴ The resultant force on the horse is $P - T$.

(a) If $P = T$ or $P < T$ there is no motion—the horse does not move the cart.

(b) If $P > T$ there is motion in a forward direction and the acceleration can be found by the usual formulæ.

Secondly, we will consider the cart.
As the cart moves there are frictional forces to overcome.
Let F represent these.
Then, the resultant force acting on the cart is $T - F$.

∴   (a) If $T = F$ there is no motion.
     (b) If $T < F$ there is no motion.
     (c) If $T > F$ the cart will move forward.

To recapitulate :
In all cases in which equal backward and forward forces are acting it is necessary to state clearly

(1) The parts of the system on which they act.
(2) The other forces which are acting within the system.

115. Worked examples.

Example 1.   *A body of mass 20 lb. is placed on a smooth horizontal table.*

(a) *Calculate the horizontal force required to move it through 20 ft. in 2·5 secs. from rest with uniform acceleration.*

(b) *A light string passing over a smooth pulley at the edge of the table is attached to the 20 lb. mass. Determine what mass must be suspended from this string to produce the motion mentioned in the first part.*

(a) For the first part we use the methods employed in examples on the Second Law of Motion (§ 112).

We first find the acceleration. The distance and time are known, so we use

$$s = \tfrac{1}{2}ft^2.$$
Substituting $20 = \tfrac{1}{2}f \times (2·5)^2,$
whence $f = \tfrac{32}{5}$ ft./sec.^{2}.

Then using the formula of § 110, viz.,

$$\frac{P}{m} = \frac{f}{g}$$

and substituting $\dfrac{P}{20} = \dfrac{\frac{32}{5}}{32}$,

whence $P = 4$ lbs. wt.

(b) The system for the second part is as shown in Fig. 127.

Let T be the tension in the string attached to the 20-lb. weight. Then by the Third Law of Motion an equal

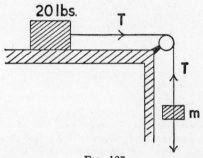

Fig. 127.

and opposite force must act on the mass m suspended from the string.

Note that m does not move downwards with an acceleration g but the whole system has the same acceleration as in the first part, viz., $\frac{32}{5}$ ft./sec.^{2}.

(1) Considering the 20-lb. body.
    Using the formula

$$\frac{P}{m} = \frac{f}{g}$$

and substituting

$$\frac{T}{20} = \frac{f}{g}$$

∴ $T = \dfrac{20f}{g}.$

(2) For the mass m, the resultant force acting on it is
$$m - T.$$

$\therefore$ With the above formula

$$\frac{m - T}{m} = \frac{f}{g}.$$

$\therefore \qquad\qquad T = m - \frac{mf}{g}.$

Equating the two values of T:

$$m - \frac{mf}{g} = \frac{20f}{g}.$$

$\therefore \qquad\qquad m(g - f) = 20f.$

$\therefore \qquad\qquad m = \frac{20f}{g - f} = \frac{20 \times \frac{32}{5}}{32 - \frac{32}{5}},$

whence $\qquad\qquad m = 5$ lbs.

Example 2. *An engine is pulling a truck along horizontal rails at a uniform velocity of 30 m.p.h., and the pull exerted on the truck is 25 lbs. wt. The pull is increased to 40 lbs. and then the acceleration is 3 ft./sec.^{2}. If the pull is increased to 50 lbs. wt. what is the acceleration?*

(1) When the velocity is uniform the resultant force must be zero (*First Law of Motion*).

$\therefore$ Forward pull of the engine is equal to the backward pull of the truck (*Third Law of Motion*).
$\therefore$ Backward pull of truck = 25 lbs. wt.

(2) When forward pull of engine increases to 40 lbs. wt.

Resultant pull of engine forward
$$= 40 - 25$$
$$= 15 \text{ lbs. wt.}$$

(3) When forward pull of engine = 50 lbs. wt.

Resultant pull of engine forward
$$= 50 - 25$$
$$= 25 \text{ lbs. wt.}$$

(4) But acceleration is proportional to applied force (*Second Law of Motion*).

∴ If f = second acceleration

$$\text{Ratio of accelerations} = \frac{f}{3},$$

$$\text{and ratio of applied forces} = \frac{25}{15}.$$

$$\therefore \qquad \frac{f}{3} = \frac{25}{15} \text{ and } f = 5 \text{ ft./sec.}^2.$$

Exercise 17.

1. A mass of 5 lbs. lies on a smooth horizontal table. It is connected by a fine string, passing over a smooth pulley on the edge of the table, to a mass of 2 lbs. hanging freely. Find the tension in the string and the acceleration of the system.

2. Masses of 1 lb. and 1 oz. are connected by a fine string passing over a smooth pulley. With what acceleration does the greater mass descend?

3. Masses of 4 lbs. and 6 lbs. are connected by a string passing over a smooth pulley. Find the tension in the string and the force required to support the pulley.

4. A mass of 8 lbs. resting on a smooth horizontal table is connected by a fine string, passing over a smooth pulley on the edge of the table, with a mass of 2 lbs. hanging freely. How far will the mass of 2 lbs. descend in 3 secs.?

5. A body of mass 200 gms. at rest on a smooth horizontal table is attached by two threads, which pass over smooth pulleys, one at each end of the table, to masses of 150 gms. and 130 gms. respectively, hanging freely. The parts of the thread on the table are aligned and parallel to the table. What is the velocity of the system 3 secs. after it is released from rest?

6. Masses of 4 lbs. and 6 lbs. connected by a light string hang on opposite sides of a smooth pulley. Find the tension in the string and the acceleration with which the system moves.

CHAPTER XI

IMPULSE AND MOMENTUM; WORK AND ENERGY; POWER

116. Impulse.

We have seen that by the Second Law of Motion we are able to measure the effect of a force by the acceleration it produces at a given instant in a known mass. We must now extend this to the examination of the effect of a force acting on a known mass for a specified time.

From the Second Law

$$\frac{P}{m} = \frac{f}{g} \quad \cdot \quad \cdot \quad \cdot \quad \cdot \quad (\S 110)$$

$$\therefore \qquad f = \frac{Pg}{m}.$$

This is an expression for the acceleration (f) produced in a mass of m lbs. by a force of P lbs. wt.

∴ Acceleration produced in t secs. is

$$\frac{Pg}{m} \times t = \frac{Pt}{m} \times g.$$

Let u be the velocity at the beginning of t secs.

„ v „ „ „ end of t secs.

Then $v - u =$ acceleration in t secs.

$$\therefore \qquad v - u = \frac{Pt}{m}g \quad \cdot \quad \cdot \quad \cdot \quad \cdot \quad \text{(from above)}$$

or $$Pt = \frac{m(v - u)}{g} \quad \cdot \quad \cdot \quad \cdot \quad \cdot \quad \text{(B)}$$

The product $P \times t$ is called the Impulse of the force. It represents the force P acting through t secs.

$\therefore$ Impulse is equal to $\dfrac{m(v-u)}{g}$.

The equation $\qquad Pt = \dfrac{m(v-u)}{g}$

is very important and will be constantly employed.

117. Impulse and momentum.

From formula (B) $Pt = \dfrac{m(v-u)}{g}$

$$= \frac{mv}{g} - \frac{mu}{g}$$

$$= \text{change of momentum.}$$

$\therefore$ The Impulse of a force in a given time is equal to the momentum it generates in the same time.

Units. In the equation

$$\frac{P}{m} = \frac{f}{g}$$

P is in lbs. wt., *i.e.*, in gravitational units.

If absolute units are employed,

$$P = mf,$$

and equation B becomes

$$Pt = m(v-u).$$

118. Worked examples.

Example 1. *A mass of 5 lbs. rests on a smooth horizontal table. What steady horizontal force will cause it in 2 secs. to move with a velocity of 2 ft./sec.?*

Since the body has no initial velocity

the formula $\qquad Pt = \dfrac{m(v-u)}{g}$

reduces to $\qquad Pt = mv$.

Let P be the unknown force. Then

$$P \times 2 = \frac{5 \times 2}{32}.$$

$\therefore \qquad\qquad P = \dfrac{5}{32}$ lbs. wt.

Example 2. *A man pushes a truck weighing $2\frac{1}{2}$ tons along horizontal rails with a steady force of 48 lbs. wt. The resistances amount to 8 lbs. per ton. Find the velocity of the truck at the end of 30 secs. and the distance moved.*

Total Resistances $= 2\frac{1}{2} \times 8$
$$= 20 \text{ lbs. wt.}$$

$\therefore$ Resultant force acting on truck $= 48 - 20$
$$= 28 \text{ lbs. wt.}$$

Mass moved $= 2\frac{1}{2}$ tons
$$= 5600 \text{ lbs.}$$

Let v be the velocity.

Then using $\qquad\qquad Pt = \dfrac{mv}{g}.$

$\therefore \qquad\qquad 28 \times 30 = \dfrac{5600v}{32},$

whence $\qquad\qquad v = \dfrac{24}{5} \text{ ft./sec.}$

To find the distance covered use

$$= \frac{u + v}{2} \times t \quad . \quad . \quad . \quad . \quad (\S\ 93)$$

whence $\qquad s = \left(\dfrac{24}{5} \div 2\right) \times 30 \quad$ (since $u = o$)
$$= 72 \text{ ft.}$$

Exercise 18.

1. A motor lorry weighing $1\frac{1}{2}$ tons is moving with a velocity of 30 m.p.h.   What force in lbs. wt. is required to bring it to rest in 12 secs.?

2. A mass of 56 lbs. is moving with a velocity of 25 ft./sec.   (*a*) Find its momentum.   (*b*) If the mass has been moving for 10 secs. what force has acted upon it?

3. A mass of 75 lbs., moving with a velocity of 16 ft./sec., is brought to rest in 2 secs. by a resisting force. What is the magnitude of the force?

4. Find the force which, acting on a mass of 40 lbs. for 12 secs., will produce a change in velocity of 20 ft./sec.

5. A force of 6 lbs. wt. acts for 8 secs. upon a mass of

24 lbs. at rest. Find the change of momentum and the final velocity of the mass.

6. The velocity of a mass of 12 lbs. is 50 ft./sec. In 4 secs. by the action of a constant force this is reduced to 30 ft./sec. What was the magnitude of the force?

119. Work.

When a body is moved against resistance by the action of a force, the force is said to do work.

Work, in this sense, is one of the most frequent occurrences of our existence. When a man lifts a weight to a height from the ground, the muscular force which he exerts does work against the force of gravity. Whenever we walk we lift our body slightly from the ground, when we climb stairs, or throw a ball into the air, work is done against gravity.

First, it is necessary to consider how it should be measured, and for this a suitable unit must be selected. When a body is lifted from the ground, work, as we have said above, is done against the force of gravity, and the amount of the work done will depend on the height through which the body is raised.

We are therefore concerned with **force** and the **distance** through which it acts.

Consequently the measurement of work must involve the units of force and distance.

This suggests that a unit of work should be a unit of force acting through a unit of distance. Hence the definition:

A unit of work in the gravitational system is the work done when a force of one pound weight overcomes resistance through a distance of one foot. This is called the foot-pound.

If, for example, a weight of 10 lbs. is raised to a height of 5 ft. from the ground, the work done is

$$10 \times 5 = 50 \text{ units of work or 50 ft.-lbs.}$$

The references to work against the force of gravity are given because this form of work is familiar to all of us. But work is done in overcoming any force. If a motor-car is travelling along a horizontal road it does very little work against gravity; the work done is against the forces of friction and air resistance. If the road slopes downward, the force of gravity does useful work and helps the motorist in overcoming resistances.

It follows from the definition of a unit of work that we may state in general terms :

(1) If a force of P lbs. wt. moves a body through 1 ft., against resistance, it does P ft.-lbs.

(2) If a force of P lbs. wt. moves a body through s ft. it does $P \times s$ units of work, *i.e.*, Ps ft.-lbs.

120. Energy. From the point of view of dynamics

Energy is the capacity to do work.

There are many forms in which energy, in this sense, may be displayed or stored. A mountain torrent rushing down the gorge may be harnessed and its energy transferred into electrical energy capable of doing work in a variety of ways. The steam pressure in the boiler possesses energy, because it moves the piston and ultimately does work in moving the train. Petrol is a source of energy by virtue of which the motor-car moves at high speed along the road. These and all other forms of energy can ultimately be divided into two kinds:

(1) **Kinetic energy.** This is the energy of a body in motion. It is the energy of the rushing stream, the ambling horse, or the wind pressing on the sails of the ship or the windmill.

(2) **Potential energy.** Energy which a body possesses by reason of its position, and which is capable of being transformed into kinetic energy is called Potential Energy. For example, the water of streams in high land may be confined by means of a dam in a reservoir. By the opening of a sluice it pours down to a lower level. In doing so it has gained kinetic energy, and so is capable of doing work.

The term " position " in the definition above must be interpreted widely, and not confined to the position of a body at a height. For example, a spring which has been wound up possesses potential energy. In the process of winding up, the positions of parts of the spring have been altered. As they resume their normal position the energy of the spring is released and changed into kinetic energy.

Petrol vapour mixed with air possesses potential energy owing to the molecules of petrol and oxygen coming into close contact. When a spark explodes the mixture the potential energy is changed into the kinetic energy which moves the car.

121. Work and energy equations.

We now proceed to find the very important dynamical equations which connect work and kinetic energy.

We have seen that a force of P lbs. wt. acting on a mass of m lbs. produces an acceleration f, as indicated in the equation

$$\therefore \qquad \frac{P}{m} = \frac{f}{g}.$$

From this $\qquad P = \frac{mf}{g}.$

If P acts through a distance s

then $\qquad Ps = \frac{m}{g} \times fs.$

Also $\qquad fs = \frac{v^2 - u^2}{2}.$

Substituting for fs in the above equation we get:

$$Ps = \frac{m(v^2 - u^2)}{2g}$$

or $\qquad Ps = \frac{1}{2} \cdot \frac{mv^2}{g} - \frac{1}{2} \frac{mu^2}{g} \quad \cdot \quad \cdot \quad \cdot \quad$ (C)

If the body starts from rest, then $u = 0$ and the equation becomes:

$$Ps = \frac{1}{2} \cdot \frac{mv^2}{g}.$$

But Ps is the work done by the force P acting through the distance s.

$\therefore \frac{1}{2} \cdot \frac{mv^2}{g}$ represents the work done on m lbs.

Conversely, if a body of weight m lbs. and having velocity v came to rest, the work done would be:

$$\tfrac{1}{2} \cdot \frac{mv^2}{g} \text{ ft.-lbs.}$$

As kinetic energy (K.E.) is defined as the capacity to do work, the expression $\tfrac{1}{2} \cdot \frac{mv^2}{g}$ is called the Kinetic Energy of the body of mass m when moving with velocity v.

In equation (C) above, the right-hand side of the equation expresses the difference between the K.E. of the body as the velocity changes from u to v.

∴ Since Ps denotes the work done

The work done is equal to the change in kinetic energy.

122. Units used for kinetic energy.

In the equation $\qquad Ps = \tfrac{1}{2}\dfrac{mv^2}{g}$

since P is measured in gravitational units.

∴ K.E. $= \tfrac{1}{2}\dfrac{mv^2}{g}$ **is in gravitation units (ft.-lbs.).**

If P were measured in poundals

Then K.E. $= \tfrac{1}{2}mv^2$ **poundals in absolute units.**

123. Energy and gravity.

Let a mass of m lbs. be raised vertically h ft. above the ground.

Then work done against gravity
$$= mh \text{ ft.-lbs.}$$

If the body now falls back to the ground

let v be its velocity on reaching the ground.

Then $\qquad v^2 = 2gh$.

But K.E. $\qquad = \tfrac{1}{2}\dfrac{mv^2}{g}$

$\qquad\qquad = \tfrac{1}{2}\dfrac{m}{g} \times 2gh$ (on substituting for v^2)

$\qquad\qquad = mh \text{ ft.-lbs.}$

∴ K.E. on reaching the ground = work done in raising it. Since in falling a distance h, the body acquires a K.E. of mh ft.-lbs.

∴ Its potential energy at a distance *h* from the ground is *mh* ft.-lbs.

∴ The potential energy of a body at a distance *h* above the ground is equal to

    (1) The work done in raising it to that height.

    (2) The K.E. acquired in falling from that height.

124. Conservation of energy.

A question which naturally occurs to a student is, What becomes of energy? A stream rushes down a valley possessing a great amount of kinetic energy. It reaches the valley, enters a placid lake, and seemingly the energy has disappeared. Experiments by scientists and engineers, as well as experience, lead to the conclusion that energy is not destroyed. That which apparently disappears is transformed into another form of energy. In this connection it should be remembered that heat is a form of energy, and there is a tendency among all other forms of energy to become transformed into heat. The theory that energy can be transformed but is indestructible and not lost to a system is called the Principle of the Conservation of Energy.

125. Summary.

The results and formulæ obtained in this chapter are of such fundamental importance that they are summarised below in a form which renders them easy for reference when problems are being worked.

(1) Equation of force and acceleration:

$$\frac{P}{m} = \frac{f}{g} \quad . \quad . \quad . \quad . \quad \text{(A)}$$

This is the expression in symbols of Newton's Second Law, upon which the whole of Dynamics is founded.

(2) Equation of impulse and momentum:

$$P \times t = \frac{m(v - u)}{g} \quad . \quad . \quad . \quad \text{(B)}$$

This is derived from (A) by multiplying both sides by *t* and substituting for *ft* on the right-hand side.

It has been called the **time effect** of a force.

(3) Equation of work and energy:

$$P \times s = \frac{m(v^2 - u^2)}{2g} \quad . \quad . \quad . \quad \text{(C)}$$

This is derived from (A) by multiplying both sides by s and substituting for fs on the right-hand side.

It has been called the distance effect of a force.

126. Worked examples.

Example I. *A bullet weighing $\frac{1}{4}$ oz. has a velocity of 1500 ft./sec. What is its kinetic energy? How far will it penetrate a fixed block, if the latter offers a constant resistance of 240 lbs. to the motion of the bullet?*

Using $\qquad$ K.E. $= \frac{1}{2}\dfrac{mv^2}{g}$.

K.E. of bullet

$$= \frac{1}{2} \times \frac{\frac{1}{64} \times (1500)^2}{32} = 550 \text{ ft.-lbs. nearly.}$$

Let s be the distance of penetration. Then using

$$Ps = \frac{1}{2} \cdot \frac{mv^2}{g} = \text{K.E. of bullet}$$

$$240 \times s = 550,$$

and $\qquad s = 2\cdot29$ ft. approx.

Example 2. *A car weighing 1 ton and travelling at 50 m.p.h. was brought to rest in 231 ft. by applying brakes. What was the frictional force in lbs. wt. exerted on the tyres by the road, assuming that it is uniform?*

The frictional force causes the body to lose the K.E., and it does work through 231 ft. The formula connecting these is

$$Ps = \frac{1}{2}\frac{mv^2}{g},$$

where $\qquad P = $ the force.

Since $\qquad$ 50 m.p.h. $= \dfrac{220}{3}$ ft./sec.

$\therefore \qquad P \times 231 = \frac{1}{2} \cdot \dfrac{2240 \times 220 \times 220}{32 \times 3 \times 3}$

whence $\qquad P = 814\cdot8$ lbs.-wt.

Example 3. *A waggon weighing 12 tons runs freely down an incline of 400 yds., the slope of which is 1 in 100. Find the kinetic energy in ft.-tons of the waggon at the bottom of the incline, neglecting friction. Find also the velocity at the end of the run.*

Length of incline = 1200 ft.

As the slope is 1 in 100, the track falls 12 ft., taking 1 in 100 as along the track and not horizontally (*see Trigonometry, § 62*).

∴   Work done = weight × distance fallen (§ 123)
    = 12 × 12 = 144 ft.-tons.

But the work done = kinetic energy acquired.

∴ $$\tfrac{1}{2}\frac{mv^2}{g} = 144$$

$$v^2 = \frac{144 \times 2 \times 32}{12},$$

whence $v = 27\cdot7$ ft./sec. (approx.).

Exercise 19.

1. Find the kinetic energy in the following cases :

(1) A mass of 24 lbs. moving with a velocity of 60 ft./sec.

(2) A mass of 2 tons moving with a velocity of 15 m.p.h.

2. A motor-cyclist with his machine weighs 300 lbs., and he is travelling at 30 m.p.h.   What is his kinetic energy?

3. What work must be done on a car weighing 400 lbs. to produce in it a velocity of 20 ft./sec.?

4. A lorry weighing 2 tons is moving with a velocity of 15 m.p.h.   What force in lbs. wt. is required to bring it to rest in 20 yds.?

5. A bullet weighing 4 oz. has a velocity of 1200 ft./sec.   In what distance will it come to rest against a resistance of 240 lbs. wt.?

6. A boy of weight 120 lbs. starts on a horizontal slide with a velocity of 12 ft./sec. and comes to rest after 20 yds.   What is the average resisting force?

7. A motor-car weighing 3000 lbs. and travelling on a level road at 30 m.p.h. is brought to rest in 20 yds.   What is the average force applied?

8. How much kinetic energy is acquired by a mass of 2 lbs. falling from rest through 50 ft.? How much kinetic energy is acquired in falling through the next 50 ft.?

9. A train weighing 400 tons is running on the level at 30 m.p.h. Then steam is shut off, and in the course of the next 300 yds. the speed is reduced to 15 m.p.h. Find in tons wt. the average resisting force.

10. What is the kinetic energy of a bullet weighing $\frac{1}{2}$ oz. and travelling with a speed of 1200 ft./sec.? What fraction of the energy has it lost after passing through a block of wood 15 ins. thick, which offers an average resistance of 400 lbs. wt.?

11. A stone weighing 100 lbs. falls from the top of a building 42 ft. high and penetrates 18 ins. into the ground before coming to rest. Find the average resistance of the ground.

12. A ship whose mass is 10,000 tons, moving with a velocity of 4 ft./sec., shuts its engines off. It travels 100 ft. before coming to rest. What was the average resistance of the water to the passage of the ship?

127. Power.

Power is the rate of doing work.

Work is expressed by Force × distance, *i.e.*, by

$$P \times s.$$

The rate at which the work is being done is expressed by the amount of work done in 1 second.

∴ If $P \times s$ units of work are done in t secs.

$$\text{Power} = \frac{Ps}{t}.$$

But
$$\frac{s}{t} = v.$$

∴ Rate at at which the force P is doing work is expressed by $P \times v$ ft.-lbs. per sec.

The unit of 1 ft.-lb. per sec. is too small for practical purpose, for example, with machines, engines, motors, etc.

Consequently the unit usually employed is the **Horse Power**, where

I Horse Power (H.P.) = 33,000 ft.-lbs. per minute,
or   550 ft.-lbs. per second.

This unit was devised by the great engineer James Watt, and it was his estimate of the rate at which a good horse could work for a few hours, though he deliberately fixed it at a high amount.

The " Horse-Power " is almost universally adopted as a rate for measuring work.

The following is a working rule for obtaining it :

Rule.   To obtain the Horse Power divide the number of ft.-lbs. of work per minute by 33,000, or the number done per second by 550.

128. Worked example.

What Horse Power is needed to draw a train of mass 200 tons up an incline of 1 in 224 at a speed of 15 m.p.h., when the frictional resistance to motion is 10 lbs. wt. per ton?

Work is done

(1) in raising the train against gravity;
(2) in overcoming frictional resistance.

Now 15 m.p.h. = 22 ft./sec.

(1) ∴ In 1 sec. the train is raised $\frac{22}{224}$ ft.
   ∴ Work done in raising the train through this height is
   $$200 \times 2240 \times \tfrac{22}{224} = 44{,}000 \text{ ft.-lbs.,}$$
   and   H.P. $= \dfrac{44{,}000}{550} = 80.$

(2) Work done against resistance
   $$= 200 \times 10 = 2000 \text{ ft.-lbs.}$$
   This acts through 22 ft. in 1 sec.
   ∴ Work done
   $$= 2000 \times 22 = 44{,}000,$$
   and H.P.
   $$= \dfrac{44{,}000}{550} = 80.$$

∴ Total H.P.
   $$= 80 + 80 = 160.$$

Exercise 20.

1. What is the H.P. of an engine which pulls a train weighing 150 tons up an incline of 1 in 100 at 30 m.p.h.? Resistances may be ignored.

2. A load of 22 cwt. was raised from a depth of 600 ft. in 4 min. from a pit. What was the H.P. developed by the engine?

3. A pump raises 120 tons of water an hour from one reservoir to another through a height of 55 ft. Neglecting any frictional resistances, what is the H.P. of the engine?

4. A gang of men in an hour raised 2000 bricks weighing 7 lbs. each, to an average height of 22 ft. What was the total H.P. developed?

5. A car was travelling on the level at 30 m.p.h. If the engine developed 9 H.P., what was the resistance to the car's motion, in lbs. wt.?

6. The resistances to a liner at high speed amount to 220 tons approximately. What H.P., to the nearest hundred, is necessary to drive the ship at 25 knots (1 knot = 6080 ft. per hour).

7. A train and locomotive weighing 270 tons are moving at 50 m.p.h. If the resistances overcome are 50 lbs. per ton, what is the H.P.?

8. Find the H.P. required to work a pump which raises 2000 lbs. of water per minute through a height of 30 ft., the water flowing away with a velocity of 10 ft./sec.

9. A man weighing 11 stone in running upstairs mounts a height of 25 ft. in 8 secs. What H.P. did he develop?

10. A car weighing 1200 lbs. accelerates on the level uniformly to 20 m.p.h. in 4 secs. If frictional resistance is equivalent to 36 lbs. wt., what is the average H.P. employed?

11. A ship requires a H.P. of 33,600 to drive it at 25 knots. What is the resistance to the ship in tons wt.?

12. A cyclist is riding at 15 m.p.h. against resistances amounting to 3 lbs. wt. What H.P. is he exerting?

CHAPTER XII

MACHINES

129. In Chapter II a " machine " was defined in the mechanical sense. The lever, one of the best known and most useful, was dealt with at some length, because the fundamental principles involved are very important, and serve as an introduction to the more general treatment of the subject which followed. Other commonly used machines will be considered in this chapter, special attention being given to their utility and efficiency.

The general principle underlying any machine is that the work which is applied to the machine from an external source is modified by the machine so that it is employed in a more advantageous way. Generally speaking the machine is used to move what is frequently called a " load ", and the external force applied to the machine is called, sometimes the " power ", sometimes the " effort ", sometimes the " applied force ".

130. Machines and work.

The relation of the load to the applied work is a very important consideration which concerns every machine. It may be expressed as follows :

Let F lbs. wt. be the effort applied to a machine.

,, s ft. be the distance its point of action is moved.

Then $(F \times S)$ ft.-lbs. wt. is the work done by the effort.

Let W lbs. be the load moved.

,, s ft. be the distance the load is moved by the machine.

Then $(W \times s)$ ft.-lbs. wt. is the work done by the load.

Then the principle of work to which we have referred states that

$$F \times S = W \times s \text{ (ignoring resistances).}$$

The principle may be expressed thus :

The work which is put into a machine is equal to the work done by the machine, together with the work done against resistances and in moving parts of the machine.

Briefly this means that more work cannot be got out of a machine than is put into it.

131. The efficiency of a machine.

If the work done by the machine were exactly equal to that put into it, then we should have a **perfectly efficient** machine, *i.e.*, no work is done which is not useful. But a certain amount of the work done is not useful, as, for example, that done against friction and in lifting some of the moving parts of the machine. The less that is lost in this way, the more efficient is the machine ; or, to put it more exactly, the ratio of the useful work done by the machine to the work put into the machine is a measure of its efficiency.

This may be expressed in the following form:

$$\text{Efficiency} = \frac{\text{useful work done by load}}{\text{total work applied}}.$$

It will be apparent from what has been said above, that this ratio will always be less than unity, and the nearer it approaches to unity, the more efficient is the machine.

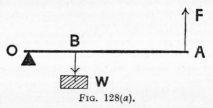

Fig. 128(a).

132. Velocity ratio.

An important factor in determining the efficiency of a machine is the " velocity ratio ". The meaning of this can readily be understood by referring to a lever.

In Fig. 128(a) *AO* represents a lever turning about a

fulcrum at O. **W lbs.** is the load, attached at B, **F lbs. wt.** is the applied effort acting at A.

Now, when A, the point of action of F, moves upward, the weight W is also moved upwards.

Let $OB'A'$ be a new position (Fig. 128(b)).

Then it is evident that the vertical distance S moved by F is greater than the vertical distance s moved by the load.

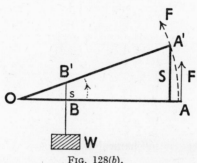

FIG. 128(b).

The ratio of these two distances is called the **velocity ratio,** or

$$\text{Velocity ratio} = \frac{\text{distance moved by effort}}{\text{distance moved by load}},$$
$$= \frac{S}{s}.$$

133. Mechanical advantage.

This is the term which is applied by engineers to express the utility of a machine. Briefly it is the ratio of the load which is moved to the applied force. It may be expressed thus:

$$\text{Mechanical advantage} = \frac{\text{load moved}}{\text{force applied}}$$
$$= \frac{W}{F}.$$

From the example shown in Fig. 128(a), and similar cases in Chapter II, we know that in general the load W is greater than F, the applied force.

G—MECH.

Hence :

(1) Velocity ratio is usually greater than unity.
(2) Mechanical advantage is usually greater than unity.
(3) Efficiency ratio is less than unity.

134. Efficiency in terms of mechanical advantage and velocity ratio.

Using the letters employed in the preceding paragraphs

$$\text{Efficiency} = \frac{\text{work done by load}}{\text{work done by effort}}$$

$$= \frac{W \times s}{F \times S} \quad \cdots \cdots \cdots \quad (\S \ 131)$$

$$= \frac{W}{F} \times \frac{s}{S}$$

$$= \frac{W}{F} \div \frac{S}{s}$$

$$= \text{mechanical advantage} \div \text{velocity ratio}$$

or

$$\text{Efficiency} = \frac{\text{mechanical advantage}}{\text{velocity ratio}}.$$

The application of the above definitions in the case of the lever is not a difficult matter, since in many cases, where no resistances are taken into account, the mechanical advantage and velocity ratio are equal. This point will be dealt with later. We shall therefore proceed to the consideration of other machines.

135. Pulleys.

In Chapter II, § 22, a brief reference was made to the pulley, but solely from the point of view of its usefulness in changing the direction of a force acting along a cord or rope. In a variety of combinations it is an invaluable machine with a wide range of usefulness.

136. Systems of pulleys.

Pulleys are often classified into three systems or orders, but only one of these is in general use. The first system is only occasionally used, but as it offers a good example of the way in which combinations may be made of pulleys, and how they may be employed to obtain a mechanical advantage, the principles involved will be briefly examined.

In Fig. 129 is shown a simple example of the combination of two pulleys A and B.

Pulley B is fixed to and supported by a beam.

Pulley A is movable, and round it passes a cord, which is fixed to the beam and then passes round both pulleys, as shown.

To A is attached a load, W., and to the free end of the rope, after it passes round pulley B, is attached a weight, P, which is sufficient to produce equilibrium.

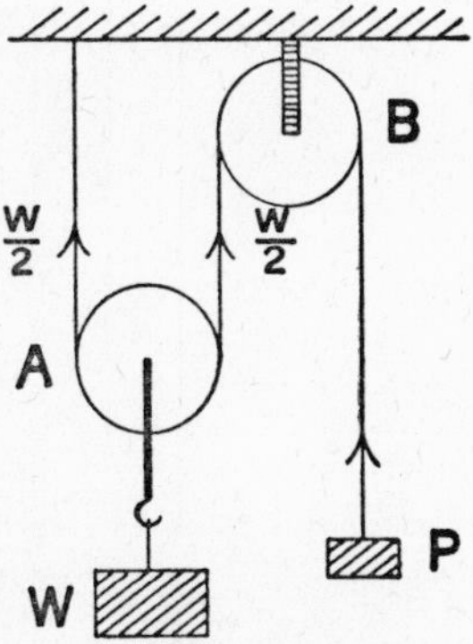

The tension in the rope is the same throughout.

Let this tension be T.

Then the weight W is supported by the two parts of the cord, in each of which the tension T acts. Each must therefore take half the load.

FIG. 129.

$$\therefore \qquad 2T = W$$

and

$$T = \frac{W}{2}.$$

But the weight, P, applied at the end of the rope to produce equilibrium must be equal to the tension in the rope, *i.e.*,

$$P = \frac{W}{2}.$$

$\therefore$ Mechanical advantage $= \dfrac{\text{load moved}}{\text{force applied}}$

$$= W \div \frac{W}{2} = 2.$$

This result ignores the resistances due to friction and

the weight of moving pulley, but it makes clear the principle involved.

It is evident also that for every foot W moves upward, P will move two feet downward.

$$\therefore \text{ Velocity ratio} = \frac{\text{distance moved by effort}}{\text{distance moved by load}} = \frac{2}{1}$$
$$= 2.$$

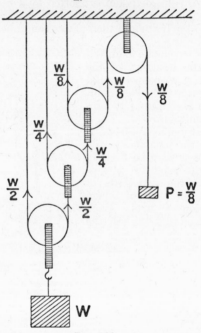

Fig. 130.

The velocity ratio will not be affected by frictional and other resistances.

By the addition of more moving pulleys, this simple example of the First Order can be extended to more complicated examples. Fig. 130 shows a succession of three movable pulleys with one fixed.

Let the load be W lbs. Then, applying the arguments of the previous example, it will be seen that the cords passing round the movable pulleys sustain in succession the weights

$$\frac{W}{2}, \frac{W}{4}, \frac{W}{8},$$

or
$$\frac{W}{2}, \frac{W}{2^2}, \frac{W}{2^3}.$$

Thus the applied force passing over the fixed pulley to maintain equilibrium is

$$\frac{W}{8} \text{ lbs. wt.}$$

$$\therefore \quad \text{Mechanical advantage} = \frac{\text{load moved}}{\text{force applied}}$$
$$= \frac{W}{\frac{W}{8}} = 8.$$

If there were a fourth movable pulley the applied force would be $\frac{W}{16}$ or $\frac{W}{2^4}$. Generally if there were n movable pulleys the applied force would be $\frac{W}{2^n}$ and the mechanical advantage would be 2^n.

This result, however, ignores friction and the force needed to raise the three movable pulleys.

Velocity ratio in the First order.

If the reasoning stated in connection with the velocity ratio of the simple combination shown in Fig. 129 be applied step by step to the succession of pulleys described in Fig. 130, it will be seen that for every foot that W is raised, P will descend 8 ft.

Thus the velocity ratio is $8 : 1$, the same as the mechanical advantage. This ratio is unaffected by the frictional resistances and the weights of the movable pulleys.

In practice, although the mechanical advantage of this system is high, the equally high velocity ratio makes it difficult to provide the necessary room for P to descend.

137. The second system of pulleys.

This is the system which is in general use. A typical arrangement is shown in Fig. 131 (a). It consists of **three fixed blocks** (the top three) fastened to a beam, with a set of **three movable**, to which the load (W) is attached. The rope is continuous; it is fastened to a hook at the bottom of the block of three movable pulleys, and then, as can be followed in the diagram, it passes **over or under** all the pulleys.

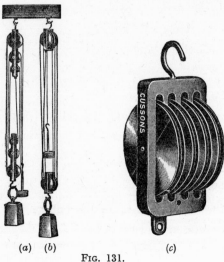

(a) (b)   (c)

Fig. 131.

The tension in the rope must therefore be the same throughout, and must be equal to the applied force (P).

The load is held up by six ropes, the same as the number of pulleys, each taking the same portion of the load, viz.,

$$\frac{W}{6}.$$

$$\therefore \quad T = \frac{W}{6}.$$

Thus the mechanical advantage is **6 : 1.**

The velocity ratio is also 6 : 1.

The weight of the movable block of pulleys and the frictional resistances are again ignored.

In practice the system usually takes the form shown in Fig. 131(b), with three movable pulleys, in which each set of pulleys, fixed and movable, is made in the form of "pulley blocks". The working of the ropes and the mechanical advantage are the same as in the form of Fig. 131(a).

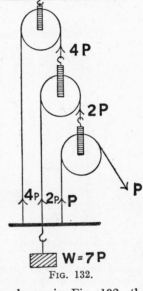

The "block" is shown in detail in Fig. 131(c).

138. The third system of pulleys.

This system is shown in Fig. 132. It consists of one pulley fixed to a beam and a number of movable pulleys arranged as shown. The cord passing over each pulley is attached to a bar, to which the weight (W) is fixed.

The share of the load taken by each string is shown in the figure, this being calculated as in the other systems.

FIG. 132.

With the three pulleys as shown in Fig. 132, the tensions in the ropes are P, $2P$, $4P$.

$$W = P + 2P + 4P$$
$$= 7P.$$

∴ The mechanical advantage is 7 : 1.

As the number of pulleys is increased the mechanical advantage increases rapidly, and becomes very high. In practice, however, the system is cumbersome and not easy to work.

139. The wheel and axle.

This useful machine is shown in Fig. 133(a).
It consists of—

(1) A large wheel (A) grooved to take a rope. This is fixed on the wheel, wound round it, and the applied force (P) acts at the free end.

(2) The axle (B), cylindrical in shape, with its diameter smaller than that of the large wheel. A rope is fixed to it and wound round in the opposite direction to that of the large wheel. To the free end is attached the load to be lifted.

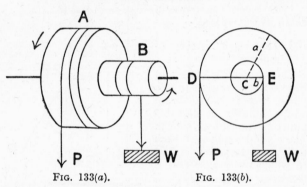

FIG. 133(a).   FIG. 133(b).

In each complete rotation of the large wheel there is one complete rotation of the axle. Consequently the applied force P acts through a distance equal to the circumference of the large wheel, while the load W is drawn up a distance equal to the circumference of the axle.

Let a be the radius of the large wheel.
   „ b „   „   „ small wheel.
Then, in one complete revolution :

Distance moved by $P = 2\pi a$.
     „   „ $W = 2\pi b$.
$\therefore$ velocity ratio $\dfrac{2\pi a}{2\pi b} = \dfrac{a}{b}$.

To find the mechanical advantage we turn to Fig. 133(b), which is an end view of the system :

DE may be regarded as a lever.

Taking moments about C, the centre of the two circles

$$P \times a = W \times b.$$

∴ Mechanical advantage

$$= \frac{W}{P} = \frac{a}{b}.$$

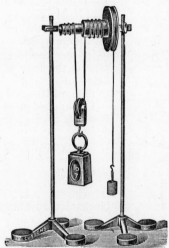

FIG. 134.

This machine is used for such purposes as drawing water from a well.

140. The differential wheel and axle.

This is a variation of the wheel and axle, with a high mechanical advantage. A representation of a model of it is shown in Fig. 134. The axle in this machine is in two parts, which are coaxial cylinders with diameters of different lengths. A rope is fixed on the smaller one, wound round it, and then wound round the larger one in the opposite direction. In the loop left between the two a movable pulley is suspended, around which the rope passes. The load is attached to this. The large wheel is rotated by means of a separate rope or a handle, on which the applied force acts.

When the large wheel is rotated, the rope winds up on the larger axle and unwinds on the smaller. The loop is thus shortened by the difference between the circumferences of the two axles. As we have seen in previous cases, the load is raised by half this difference.

Let a = radius of large axle.
  „ b =   „   small axle.
  „ R =   „   large wheel.

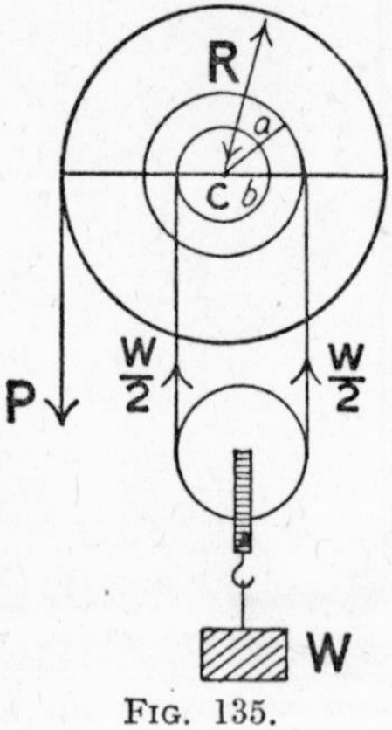

In one complete rotation the rope in the loop is shortened by $2\pi(a - b)$.

∴ Load is raised by $\pi(a - b)$.

The applied force in one rotation acts through $2\pi R$.

$$\therefore \quad \text{velocity ratio} = \frac{2\pi R}{\pi(a - b)}$$
$$= \frac{2R}{a - b}.$$

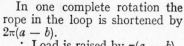

Mechanical advantage.

We proceed by the method used for the simple wheel and axles. Fig. 135 shows an end view of the wheel and the two axles, C being the centre of the three circles.

Fig. 135.

Taking moments about C

$$P \times R = \frac{W}{2}(a - b).$$
$$\therefore \qquad P = \frac{W(a - b)}{2R}.$$
$$\therefore \qquad \frac{W}{P} = \frac{2R}{a - b}.$$
$$\therefore \qquad M.A. = \frac{2R}{a - b}.$$

This can be made very high by making the difference between *a* and *b* very small.

141. The inclined plane.

An inclined plane and its special form the wedge may be regarded as machines, since it is possible by means of them for a load to be raised by a smaller applied force. In the inclined plane
ABC (Fig. 136)

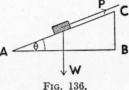

Let $AC = l$.
,, $BC = h$.
When a load is moved along the length of the plane, l, it is raised vertically through the height h.

FIG. 136.

$$\therefore \quad \text{The velocity ratio} = \frac{l}{h}.$$

Let P be applied force.
and W ,, load.

Then $$P \times AC = W \times BC.$$

$$\therefore \qquad \frac{W}{P} = \frac{AC}{BC} = \frac{l}{h}.$$

$$\therefore \qquad M.A. = \frac{l}{h}.$$

In actual practice friction offers a considerable resistance. This has been previously examined (*see* § 81).

It is because of the mechanical advantage involved that we take a zig-zag path when climbing a hill.

The wedge is a double inclined plane.

142. The screw.

The principle of the inclined plane is that upon which a screw is constructed. This will be made evident by the following simple experiment.

Cut out in paper a right-angled triangle *ABC* (Fig. 137(*a*)). This represents the side view of an inclined plane.

Wrap this round a suitable cylinder such as a pencil

or a small cylindrical bottle. It will be seen that the edge AB will form a spiral curve round the cylinder in the same way that the thread of a screw winds round the screw shaft. This is represented in Fig. 137(b)).

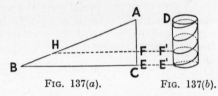

FIG. 137(a).   FIG. 137(b).

The distance between two points, such as E' and F', where the spiral cuts a straight line DE', parallel to the axis of the cylinder, is called the " pitch " of the screw.

When a complete turn of the screw is made, the work done in overcoming resistance, or in raising a weight, as in the case of the screw-jack, is equal to the work done by the applied force acting through the vertical distance EF or through the corresponding distance BH on the inclined plane.

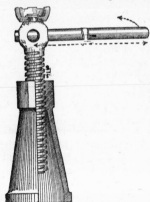

FIG. 138.

143. The screw-jack.

In the screw-jack the principle of the screw is utilised, as indicated above, to lift heavy weights.

The effort is usually applied at the end of a long handle-bar (*see* Fig. 138). One complete revolution of the handle raises the load through a vertical distance equal to the pitch of the screw.

Thus if the bar handle be **12** ins. long and the pitch of the screw be $\frac{1}{2}$ in., then—

Distance through which applied force acts

$$= 2\pi \times 12 \text{ ins.}$$

Distance the load is raised

$$= \tfrac{1}{2} \text{ in.}$$

∴ Velocity ratio

$$= 2\pi \times 12 \div \tfrac{1}{2} = 150 \text{ approx.}$$

The mechanical advantage is also high. By increasing the length of the handle-bar and keeping the pitch small very large weights can be raised by comparatively small applied forces.

144. The efficiency of a machine.

In § 134 it was stated that the efficiency of a machine is expressed as follows :

$$\text{Efficiency} = \frac{\text{mechanical advantage}}{\text{velocity ratio}}.$$

Now that the working of a few machines has been examined, we must return to further consideration of the question of efficiency.

In most machines the velocity ratio is readily determined by finding :

(1) How far the load has been raised.

(2) The distance through which the applied force moves.

If the efficiency were perfect, *i.e.*, 100 per cent., then the ratio of mechanical advantage to velocity ratio would be unity.

But, while the velocity ratio is independent of the load, the mechanical advantage does vary for different loads, since the frictional resistances are not constant, but vary with the load.

The efficiency of a machine was defined in § 131 in the form :

$$\text{Efficiency} = \frac{\text{useful work done by load}}{\text{total work applied}}.$$

If the machine were perfect, the useful work is equal to the total work applied. But there is a loss of useful work, and so of efficiency, owing to resistances. Consequently the efficiency ratio is less than unity.

This ratio is usually expressed as a percentage. If, for example, the efficiency ratio were $\frac{7}{10}$ this would be expressed as a 70 per cent. efficiency. The meaning of this is that 30 per cent. of the useful work has been lost owing to resistances.

It should be remembered that, as stated above, when the machine is perfect the ratio

$$\frac{\text{mechanical advantage}}{\text{velocity ratio}},$$

which also expresses the efficiency, is also equal to unity. Consequently for the perfect machine

Mechanical advantage = velocity ratio.

145. The law of the machine.

It is important that we should know the efficiency of a machine, and hence we must know the law which connects the load and effort. Such a law is called the "law of the machine" and takes into account frictional and other resistances. In a great many cases, for reasons given in the preceding paragraph, this can be obtained only by experiment. This involves obtaining a series of corresponding values of "Load" and "Effort" and plotting them on squared paper. From the graph the law can be determined by methods given below.

We shall confine ourselves to those cases in which the graph is a straight line, and the law is a linear law, *i.e.*, of the first degree.

The general form of it will be:

$$E = aW + b,$$

where E represents the applied force
and W „ „ load.

In this equation the quantities to be determined are the constants a and b, because when these are known the law can be written down.

If, for example, we find that $a = 0.56$ and $b = 1.4$, then the law of the machine is

$$E = 0.56W + 1.4.$$

This can then be used to find P when W is known or vice versa.

The constant " b " is the value of P when $W = 0$; it is the value of the resistance which has to be overcome to start the machine when there is no load at all.

An example of the application of the graphical method of obtaining a solution is given below. It is taken from Vol. I of *National Certificate Mathematics* (published by the English Universities Press). Those students who have no experience of graphical methods should first study Chapter VII in the book mentioned.

146. Worked example.

In a series of experiments carried out with a Weston Differential Pulley, the effort E lb. necessary to raise a load of W lb. was found to be as follows.

W . .	10	20	30	40	50
E . .	3·3	4·8	6·4	7·9	9·5

Show these values on a graph and determine the law which they seem to follow, and find the probable effort when the load is 25 lbs.

Examining the data, and noting the maximum number to be plotted in each case, we can take 0·5 in. on the horizontal axis to represent 10 lbs. for the load W, and 0·25 in. to represent 1 lb. for the effort E.

Then plot the points as shown (Fig. 139). Since the data are derived from experimental results, slight deviations from a straight line are to be expected. If any one or two points are definitely not in accordance with the majority, they should be neglected.

A straight line should be drawn to take in as many of the points as possible, or, failing that, it should be so drawn, that the points are fairly evenly distributed on either side of it.

We now take two points A and B on this line, which are suitable for reading off the values. They will not necessarily be either of the points actually plotted, and it is advisable to choose them fairly wide apart.

The quantities E and W are evidently connected by a linear law which will be of the form

$$E = mW + b.$$

For the point A, $W = 35$ lbs. and $E = 7\cdot2$ lbs.
For the point B, $W = 12$ lbs. and $E = 3\cdot6$ lbs.

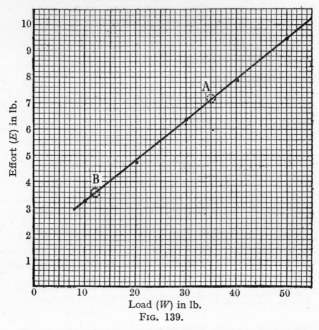

Fig. 139.

Hence, substituting in $E = mW + b$, because these values satisfy the required law, we have :

(1) $7\cdot2 = 35m + b$.
(2) $3\cdot6 = 12m + b$.

Subtracting,

$$3\cdot6 = 23m$$

that is

$$m = \frac{3\cdot6}{23} = \frac{18}{115} = 0\cdot157$$

$$= 0\cdot16 \text{ approx.}$$

Substituting in (2),
$$3\cdot6 = 12m + b$$
$$3\cdot6 = \frac{12 \times 18}{115} + b.$$
$$\therefore \quad b = 3\cdot6 - 1\cdot88$$
$$= 1\cdot72.$$

Hence the law is $E = 0\cdot16W + 1\cdot72$.
To find E when the load is 25 lbs., substitute in this law thus determined.

Then
$$E = 0\cdot157 \times 25 + 1\cdot72$$
$$= 5\cdot6 \text{ lbs. approx.}$$

This result agrees very closely with the graph itself.

147. Algebraical method.

The algebraical working employed in the graphical solution, described above, is the usual method of finding the law when two pairs of values of the load and effort are given.

If the law of the machine is known to be of the form $E = aW + b$, and two corresponding values of E and W are known, then on substituting these values in $E = aW + b$ two equations involving a and b as unknowns are obtained and these can be solved simultaneously.

148. Worked examples.

Example 1. *The quantities E and W are connected by the equation $E = aW + b$. It is known that when*
$$W = 5, E = 1\cdot5$$
and when
$$W = 10, E = 3\cdot6.$$

Find the law of the machine.

Substituting the corresponding values of E and W in
$$E = aW + b$$
we get
$$1\cdot5 = 5a + b \quad . \quad . \quad . \quad . \quad (1)$$
and
$$3\cdot6 = 10a + b \quad . \quad . \quad . \quad . \quad (2)$$
Subtracting
$$2\cdot1 = 5a.$$
$$\therefore \quad a = 0\cdot42.$$

Substituting this value for (a) in equation (2), we get :
$$3 \cdot 6 = 10 \times 0 \cdot 42 + b,$$
whence $\qquad b = 3 \cdot 6 - 4 \cdot 2.$
$\therefore \qquad b = -0 \cdot 6.$

Substituting these values for a and b in $E = aW + b$, we get :
$$E = 0 \cdot 42W - 0 \cdot 6.$$

This is the law of the machine.

Example 2. *The velocity ratio of a screw-jack is 60. Its efficiency is 30 per cent. What effort is needed to lift a load of 1 ton with this jack?*

Let E be the effort required in lb. wt.

From § 144 :

$$\text{Percentage efficiency} = \frac{\text{mechanical advantage}}{\text{velocity ratio}} \times 100.$$

$\therefore \qquad 30 = \dfrac{\text{M.A.}}{60} \times 100,$

whence $\qquad \text{M.A.} = 18.$

Also $\qquad \text{M.A.} = \dfrac{\text{load}}{\text{applied force}}.$

$\therefore \qquad 18 = \dfrac{2240}{E}.$

$\therefore \qquad 18E = 2240$

and $\qquad E = 124\frac{4}{9}$ lbs. wt.

149. Summary.

A summary of important formulæ is printed below for convenient reference when working problems in the exercise which follows :

(1) Velocity Ratio
$$= \frac{\text{distance moved by applied force}}{\text{distance moved by load}}.$$

(2) Mechanical Advantage
$$= \frac{\text{load}}{\text{applied force}}.$$

(3) Per cent. Efficiency
$$= \frac{\text{mechanical advantage}}{\text{velocity ratio}} \times 100.$$

Exercise 21.

1. In a machine a weight of 80 lbs. was moved by an applied force of 25 lbs. moving through 10 ft. The load moved through 3 ft.

Find (a) the velocity ratio; (b) the mechanical advantage; (c) the percentage efficiency.

2. In a certain machine a load of 160 lbs. wt. is lifted by 28 lbs. wt., and the velocity ratio is 8. Find the percentage efficiency.

3. In a machine the load is 400 lbs. and there is an efficiency of 64 per cent. If the velocity ratio is 5, find the applied force.

4. In a differential wheel and axle the radius of the large wheel was 10 ins., and the radii of the two cylindrical parts of the axle were 2 ins. and $1\frac{1}{2}$ ins. respectively. The efficiency of the machine is 60 per cent. If the load to be lifted is 200 lbs. wt., what applied force is necessary?

5. It is required to lift a load of 500 lbs. by a screw-jack in which the efficiency at that load is known to be 25 per cent. If the velocity ratio is 150, find the applied force and the mechanical advantage.

6. A load of 1 ton was drawn through a quarter of a mile up an inclined plane of slope 1 in 30. The force applied was 500 lbs. wt. parallel to the plane. Find the efficiency of the plane, regarded as a machine.

7. A screw has three threads to the inch, and the effort is applied at the end of an arm 1 ft. long. What force must be applied to lift a load of 2 cwt. if the efficiency at that load is 25 per cent.?

8. In a screw-jack the effort, E, required to lift a load W is applied at the end of a handle which describes a circle of 7 ins. radius. The pitch of the screw is $\frac{1}{2}$ in. What is the velocity ratio? ($\pi = \frac{22}{7}$.) What is the efficiency if an effort of 5 lbs. wt. will lift a load of 1 cwt.?

9. In an experiment on an inclined plane it was found that a force of $6\frac{1}{2}$ lbs. wt., applied up the plane and parallel to it, was required to haul a 10-lbs. mass slowly up the plane. If the inclination of the plane is 30° and its length 6 ft., find (a) the work against gravity; (b) the work done against friction, when the mass is pulled the whole length of the plane; (c) the efficiency of this plane considered as a simple machine?

10. In certain experiments carried out with a machine the effort E and the load W were found to have the values as set out below. The law connecting E and W is of the form $E = aW + b$, where a and b are constants. Plot the values below and find the law.

W . .	30	40	60	70	80
E . .	2·13	2·6	3·8	4·3	5·1

11. In an experiment on a crane the load lifted (W lbs.) and the corresponding effort (E lbs.) required were found as under.

W . .	14	42	84	112
E . .	5·1	13·3	26·0	35·3

Assuming that E and W are connected by a law of the form $E = aW + b$, where a and b are constants, find the values of a and b.

12. The following table gives the result of an experiment. Plot the load–effort diagram and determine the equation (of the form $E = aW = b$) which most nearly accords with the results.

W (in lbs.)	7	14	21	28	35	42	49	56
E (in lbs.)	3	6·5	9·5	12·5	16	18·75	22	25

13. In experiments with a screw-jack the following results were obtained :

Load .	100	120	140	160	180	200
Effort .	12·6	13·8	15·7	17·6	19·6	21·5

Plot these, and from your diagram find the values of a and b in the law which connects the load and effort, viz., $E = aW + b$.

14. The effort (E) and the load (W) of a certain machine are connected by a law of the form $E = aW + b$. It is known that when $W = 6$, $E = 5 \cdot 9$, and when $W = 10$, $E = 7 \cdot 5$. Find a and b and write down the law.

CHAPTER XIII

COMPOSITION OF VELOCITIES ; RELATIVE VELOCITY

150. Composition of velocities

Just as a body may be acted upon by more than one force, so it may have imparted to it more than one velocity. A simple example may make this clear.

Suppose a man to be moving across the deck of a

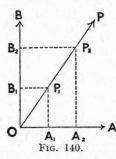

FIG. 140.

moving ship at right angles to the axis of the ship, and therefore at right angles to the direction in which the ship is moving.

Let the man start from O (Fig. 140) and at the end of 2 secs. have moved to A_1, where $OA_1 = a$ ft.

During the 2 secs. the ship will have moved a distance relative to the sea in the direction OB. Let this distance be represented by OB_1, where $OB_1 = b$ ft.

These two displacements OA_1 and OB_1 in the directions OA and OB respectively are equivalent to a single displacement OP_1 in the direction OP. Relative to the sea the man will have moved through OP_1.

Similarly in the next 2 secs. Suppose the man to have moved to A_2 in the direction OA and to B_2 in the direction OB. The man's position relative to the sea will be P_2 and he will thus have moved through P_1P_2, assuming both his velocity and that of the ship to be uniform.

Thus in 4 secs. the man will have moved, relative to the sea, through the distance OP_2. Therefore, he has a velocity along OP which will be equal to $\dfrac{OP_2}{4}$ ft. per second.

Using the same term which is adopted when a body is acted upon by two forces, we can say that the velocity of the man along *OP* is the **resultant of the velocities** along *OA* and *OB*.

The velocity of an aeroplane is a striking example of the composition of velocities. It possesses the velocity due to the engines in the direction set by the aviator and, in addition, a velocity which is imparted by the force of the wind. This must be ascertained in magnitude and direction before it is possible to learn the exact direction and velocity with which the aeroplane is moving.

There is another instance in which the actual direction of the resultant velocity is apparent to an observer.

Suppose a man starts to row a boat across a stream with a strong current and points his boat directly at the opposite bank (*see* Fig. 141). The current imparts to his boat an additional velocity down-stream and at right angles to the velocity which he gives to the boat as a result of his rowing. As a consequence of having these two simultaneous velocities, he

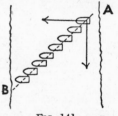

FIG. 141.

actually moves with a resultant velocity, as shown in Fig. 141, the direction of which will be along a straight line such as *AB*. It would be a matter of calculation, which will be discussed in this chapter, in what direction he must point the boat if he is to arrive at a point on the other bank directly opposite to *A*.

151. The parallelogram of velocities.

The student will be prepared to learn that, just as when two forces act on a body their resultant can be found by means of the law of the " parallelogram of force ", so if a body receives two velocities, these have a **resultant velocity** which can be determined by a corresponding parallelogram law. This is known as the Parallelogram of Velocities, and is defined as follows :

Parallelogram of velocities.

When a body has two simultaneous velocities and these are represented in magnitude and direction by two adjacent sides of a parallelogram, their resultant velocity is represented in magnitude and direction by the diagonal of the parallelogram which passes through their point of intersection.

The " Parallelogram of Force " was established as a result of experiments, and no mathematical proof was given. Experimental demonstration of the parallelogram of velocities, however, is not easy or satisfactory, and it is not proposed at this stage to burden the student with a mathematical proof. The parallelogram law applies to all vector quantities, and its truth will be assumed.

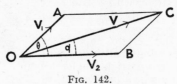

Fig. 142.

152. Calculation of a resultant velocity.

The resultant of two velocities is found in the same way as the resultant of two forces.

Let OA, OB (Fig. 142) represent two velocities imparted to a body.

Let θ be the angle between them.

Complete the parallelogram $OACB$.

Draw the diagonal OC.

Then OC represents the resultant of the velocities represented by OA and OB.

(1) **To find the value of OC.** Using the rule proved in § 45

$$OC^2 = OA^2 + OB^2 + 2OA \cdot OB \cos AOB.$$

Let v_1 and v_2 represent the velocities.

  „ V be their resultant.

Then, on substitution

$$V^2 = v_1{}^2 + v_2{}^2 + 2v_1v_2 \cos \theta.$$

(2) To find α, the angle between the resultant and v_2, as in § 45 :

$$\tan \alpha = \frac{v_1 \sin \theta}{v_2 + v_1 \cos \theta}.$$

Note.—It is a good plan to check the working by finding also the angle between v_1 and the resultant. If this be β, then :

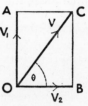

$$\tan \beta = \frac{v_2 \sin \theta}{v_1 + v_2 \cos \theta}.$$

When the directions of the velocities are at right angles.

As will be seen from Fig. 143,

Fig. 143.

$$\text{Resultant velocity} = \sqrt{v_1{}^2 + v_2{}^2}.$$

Also
$$v_2 = V \cos \theta$$
$$v_1 = V \sin \theta.$$

153. Component velocities.

A velocity can be resolved into two component velocities by the method employed to obtain components of a force. The most useful case is that in which we require to obtain two components at right angles. The method again is the same as for forces, and will be evident from an examination of Fig. 143.

If V be the velocity of which it is desired to find components making angles of θ and 90° − θ with it, the components will be :

$$V \cos \theta, \ V \sin \theta.$$

154. Worked example.

In order that the pilot of an aeroplane may reach his destination at a specified time, it is necessary, after making allowances for the strength and direction of the wind, that he should travel at 180 m.p.h. at an angle 30° E. of N. The wind is blowing from the south at 40 m.p.h. In what direction and with what velocity must he set his course?

Note.—As was the case when dealing with problems

on forces, problems may usually be solved either (1) by accurate drawing, or (2) by trigonometry.

In this problem it will be seen that we know the magnitude and direction of the Resultant velocity—viz., 180 m.p.h. at 30° E. of N. We also know one of the components—viz., the velocity of the wind, 40 m.p.h. from the south.

Construction.

Draw *OA* on a suitable scale to represent velocity of wind (Fig. 144).

Draw *OB* making 30° with *OA* and to represent 180 m.p.h. on the scale chosen.

This represents the Resultant Velocity.

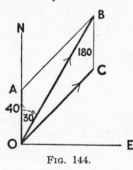

FIG. 144.

Join *AB*.

Complete the parallelogram *OABC*.

Then *OC* represents the other component—*i.e.*, the magnitude of the velocity with which the aviator starts and the direction in which he points the machine.

We need therefore to find :

(1) The magnitude of *OC*.
(2) The angle it makes with the north or east.

This can be done by means of a carefully drawn figure or

We can obtain the solution by trigonometry, as follows :

It is necessary to solve △*OBC* or △*OAB*.

This is the case of " two sides and included angle " (*Trigonometry*, p. 124).

The cosine rule may be used, or if we wish to employ logs, the formula

$$\tan \frac{B - C}{2} = \frac{b - c}{b + c} \cot \frac{A}{2}$$

is better.

The solution by this means is given as an example.
Using the form
$$\tan \frac{A - B}{2} = \frac{a - b}{a + b} \cot \frac{C}{2},$$

let $\angle OAB = A,$

then $a = 180.$

Let $\angle ABO = B,$

then $b = 40.$

Let $\angle AOB = C.$

∴ Substituting in the above formula
$$\tan \frac{A - B}{2} = \frac{180 - 40}{180 + 40} \cot \frac{30°}{2}$$
$$= \frac{140}{220} \cot 15°.$$

Taking logs

$\log \tan \dfrac{A - B}{2} = \log 140 + \log \cot 15° - \log 220$

	no.	log.
	140°	2·1461
	cot 15	0·5719
		2·7180
	220	2·3424
	log tan 67° 10′	0·3756

$\quad\quad\quad\quad\quad = 0·3756$

$\quad\quad\quad\quad\quad = \log \tan 67° 10'.$

∴ $\dfrac{A - B}{2} = 67° 10'$

and $A - B = 134° 20'.$

Also $A + B = 150°.$

Adding $2A = 284° 20'.$

∴ $A = 142° 10'.$

Subtracting $2B = 15° 40'.$

∴ $B = 7° 50'.$

∴ $\angle AOC = 30° + 7° 50'$
$$= 37° 50'.$$

∴ Direction of course is 37° 50′ E. of N.

To find AB:

Using the sine rule :
$$\frac{AB}{\sin 30} = \frac{40}{\sin 7° 50'}.$$

∴ $AB = \dfrac{40 \sin 30°}{\sin 7° 50'} = \dfrac{20}{\sin 7° 50'}$

$\quad\quad\quad\quad\quad [\sin 30° = \tfrac{1}{2}].$

	no.	log.
	20	1·3010
	sin 7° 50′	$\bar{1}$·1345
	146·8	2·1665

Using logs as shown in working
$$AB = 146·8 \text{ or } 147 \text{ approx.}$$

∴ The pilot must set his course at 37° 50′ E. of N. at 147 m.p.h. approx.

Exercise 22.

1. Find the resultants of the following pairs of velocities and the angle each of them makes with the direction of the larger velocity in each case :

(a) 12 ft./sec. and 8 ft./sec. Angle between them 60°.

(b) 10 m.p.h. and 12 m.p.h. Angle between them 40°.

2. A ship is steaming at 15 m.p.h. and a man walks across the deck at 3 m.p.h., in a direction at right angles to the axis of the ship. What is the direction and magnitude of the man's resultant velocity relative to the sea ?

3. A ship is heading west at 12 knots. A current deflects it so that it actually travels in a direction 20° N. of W. at 15 knots. What are the magnitude and direction of the current ?

4. A river 2 miles wide flows with a speed of 1 m.p.h. Find the time required for a man swimming with a speed of 2 m.p.h. to cross the river at right angles to the bank.

5. The time fixed for an aeroplane to fly to a certain town is 3 hours. The town is 240 miles due east of the starting point, and the wind is blowing from the S.E. at 30 m.p.h. Find the direction in which the pilot must head his aeroplane and the necessary velocity.

6. The pilot of an aeroplane which flies at 100 m.p.h. when there is no wind, wishes to travel due north when a wind is blowing at 20 m.p.h. towards the east. Find graphically the direction in which he must point the nose of the machine, and his actual speed relative to the ground.

7. An aeroplane has to fly 300 miles due north. Its normal velocity is 150 m.p.h. and a wind is blowing from the south-west at 30 m.p.h. How long must the pilot allow for the journey, flying at his normal velocity ?

8. If a velocity of 60 m.p.h. is resolved into two components at right angles to one another, find them when they are in the ratio of 3 : 4.

155. Relative velocity.

It will be helpful in understanding what is termed relative velocity if the student will recall some of the sensations which he has probably experienced when, travelling in a train, another train has been moving on the next set of rails.

(1) Suppose that the trains were moving in the same direction, yours at 20 m.p.h., the other at 25 m.p.h. The other train appears to be moving very slowly; sometimes, even if the running is very smooth, the other train may seem to stand still while yours is moving backwards. The motion which the other train seems to possess is called the **Relative velocity** of the other train with respect to yours. The velocity with which the other train seems to be moving will clearly depend on the difference between the velocities of the two trains. If the velocities were as stated above, and it were possible for you to measure the velocity with which the other train seems to move—*i.e.*, its relative velocity, this would be 5 m.p.h. in the direction in which you are both going.

To a man in the other train, your train, on the contrary, will appear to be moving backwards at 5 m.p.h. This would be the relative velocity of your train with respect to the other.

It should be noted that **if the velocities of both trains were to be increased by the same amount**, the relative velocities would be the same. If, for example, each were to be increased by 10 m.p.h. to 30 m.p.h. and 35 m.p.h. respectively, the relative velocity would still be 5 m.p.h.

(2) Suppose the trains were moving in **opposite directions**, yours moving north at 20 m.p.h., the other moving south at 25 m.p.h. At the end of an hour, if the trains continued to move uniformly, your train would have travelled 20 miles north, while the other would have gone 25 miles south. The two trains would be $(20 + 25)$—*i.e.*, 45 miles apart. They would have separated at the rate of 45 m.p.h.

Each train is moving relatively to the other at **45** m.p.h. This is therefore the **Relative velocity**.

Now let us approach the question in another way. Suppose that each train were to receive an additional velocity equal and opposite to that of the north-bound train—viz. 20 m.p.h.

Then the train going north would have no velocity—*i.e.*, it would be at rest.

But the velocity of the south-bound train would be equal to 20 + 25, or 45 m.p.h. south.

Then, to the north-bound train the south-bound train would appear to be moving south at 45 m.p.h.

∴ The Relative velocity of the south-bound train with reference to the one going north is 45 m.p.h.

In a similar way the relative velocity of the north-

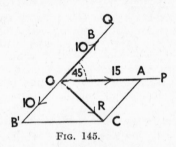

Fig. 145.

bound train with reference to the train going south could be found.

156. Relative velocities of bodies starting from the same point and diverging.

Suppose that two cyclists P and Q start from a point O (Fig. 145) and travelling as follows,

P along OP at 15 m.p.h.
Q　,,　OQ at 10 m.p.h.

How does P appear to Q to be moving?

Or what is the relative velocity of P with respect to Q?

Let us adopt the device which was employed in case of trains moving along parallel lines.

The method may be stated thus :

"*Apply to each a velocity equal and opposite to the velocity of one of them, say Q. Then Q will be brought to* *rest. The resultant velocity of P will be the relative velocity of P with respect to Q.*

In accordance with this we apply to each a velocity equal and opposite to Q's velocity—which is 10 m.p.h. along OQ.

Let OB represent Q's velocity.

,, OA ,, P's ,,

Then OB' equal and opposite to OB represents the velocity added to each.

As a consequence Q will be at rest.

The velocity of P will be the resultant of

15 m.p.h. along OP—*i.e.*, OA

and 10 ,, ,, OB'.

Complete the parallelogram $OACB.'$

Then the diagonal OC represents in magnitude and direction the resultant of the two velocities represented by OA and OB'.

Or OC represents in magnitude and direction the relative velocity of P with respect to Q.

This may be measured or calculated as shown in § 150.

As an exercise the student should draw the construction for obtaining the relative velocity of Q with respect to P.

This will be done by applying to each a velocity equal and opposite to the velocity of P.

Definition.—*The relative velocity of P with respect to Q is the velocity, both in magnitude and direction, with which P appears to Q to be moving.*

157. Relative velocity of bodies not diverging from the same point.

The following example will illustrate this case and indicate the method of solution.

A ship A (see Fig. 146) is moving due north at 15 knots. A ship, B, 10 miles due north, is moving west at 10 knots. What is the relative velocity of A with respect to B?

The positions of the ships are indicated in Fig. 146.

To the velocity of each add a velocity equal and opposite to that of B—*i.e.*, we add a velocity of 10 knots east.

Then B is relatively at rest.

The resultant of the two velocities now imparted to A

is the resultant of the velocities represented by DA and CA.

Complete the rectangle $ACED$. Then the diagonal EA represents the resultant of the two velocities.

∴ EA represents in magnitude and direction the relative velocity of A with respect to B.

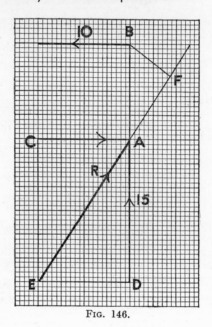

Fig. 146.

These can now be determined by drawing or by calculation.

By calculation

$$AE = \sqrt{15^2 + 10^2}$$
$$= \sqrt{325}$$
$$= 18 \text{ nearly.}$$

Also $\tan CAE = \dfrac{15}{10} = 1\cdot5$.

∴ $\angle CAE = 56° 19'$.

∴ The relative velocity of A with respect to B is 18 knots in a direction 56° 19′ N. of E.

It should be noted that if EA be produced, since it represents the path of A relative to B, by drawing BF perpendicular to EA, the length of BF represents the shortest distance between A and B as they move on their respective paths.

Exercise 23

1. Two men, A and B, meet at cross-roads and proceed up two different roads, A going due north and B going due east, at 3 m.p.h. and 4 m.p.h. respectively. What is the relative velocity of B with respect to A ?

2. A ship A is moving E. 30° N. at 12 m.p.h.   A second ship B is moving S. 30° W. at 9 m.p.h.   What is the velocity of A relative to B ?

3. A train A travels due north at 30 m.p.h. and a train B due west at 40 m.p.h.   What is the velocity of A relative to B ?

4. A motor is travelling due east at 30 m.p.h.   A train appears to be travelling due north with a velocity of 60 m.p.h.   What is the true velocity of the train ?

5. A steamer A is 10 miles due south of a steamer B. A is moving in a northerly direction at 12 m.p.h., and B is moving to the west at 9 m.p.h.   Find the velocity of A with respect to B.   Find also from a diagram, drawn to scale, how near A will approach to B.

6. A body is moving north with a velocity of 20 m.p.h., and its velocity relative to another body B appears to be 30 m.p.h. in a north-easterly direction.   Find the velocity of B in magnitude and direction.

7. A ship is sailing due west with a velocity of 12 knots ; while another is steaming south-east at the rate of 18 knots.   Find graphically the magnitude and direction of the velocity of the second ship relative to the first.

CHAPTER XIV

PROJECTILES

158. The path of a projectile.

Everybody is familiar with the fact that when a cricket ball, or a rocket, or a jet of water from a hose-pipe is impelled into the air, the path which it describes is a curve.

This curve is a **parabola**, and the path described is called the **trajectory**.

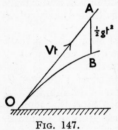

FIG. 147.

In each case there is an impelling force whose direction is inclined to the vertical. If it were otherwise we know that a body projected vertically upwards moves in a straight line to a highest point and then descends vertically to its starting point.

Let V denote the velocity imparted to a projectile by an impelling force.

From the moment that the body begins to move upwards it is acted upon by the force of gravity and its velocity decreases.

Consider its position after t secs.

Under the action of the impelling force, it will have moved a distance Vt in the direction in which it was projected (represented by OA in Fig. 147).

Under the action of gravity, during the interval, it will have fallen a distance $\frac{1}{2}gt^2$ vertically downwards, represented by AB.

If a series of values of t were taken, corresponding points, such as B, would be obtained, all of which lie on the curve.

159. Components of the initial velocity.

Let V be the velocity of projection.

Let α be the angle of projection made with the horizontal.

Resolve V into vertical and horizontal components

Horizontal component $= V \cos \alpha$ (Fig. 148).

Vertical component $= V \sin \alpha$.

The horizontal component, $V \cos \alpha$.

This is unaffected by the force of gravity, being at right angles to it. Therefore

It remains constant throughout the flight.

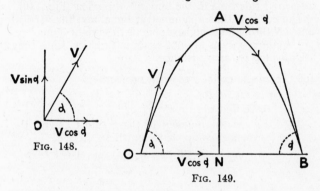

FIG. 148.

FIG. 149.

$\therefore$ After any time t, distance covered $= V \cos \alpha \times t$.
The vertical component, $V \sin \alpha$.

This is subject to a retardation due to the force of gravity.

$\therefore$ After time t, it becomes $V \sin \alpha - gt$.
The vertical distance described after time t is

$$V \sin \alpha \times t - \tfrac{1}{2}gt^2$$

(1) When $gt = V \sin \alpha$, *i.e.*, the vertical component is equal to zero, the body projected is at the **highest point** of the curve (A in Fig. 149).

At that point the only velocity which the body has is the horizontal component, $V \cos \alpha$.

(2) After the highest point the body moves along the

downward part, its vertical component subject to the acceleration due to gravity and with horizontal velocity, $V \cos \alpha$ (Fig. 149).

(3) The body reaches the ground again at B with a velocity which is the resultant of its horizontal and vertical velocities,

viz., $\qquad$ $V \cos \alpha$ horizontal,
$\qquad$ $- V \sin \alpha$ vertical.

Consequently the velocity with which it strikes the ground is the same in magnitude as the initial velocity—viz., V.

The angle which V makes with the horizontal is α, measured this time in the opposite direction (Fig. 149).

The curve is thus a symmetrical one, and the vertical line AN through the highest point is the axis of symmetry.

The above results are not exact in practice, since they are affected by air resistance.

160. Formulae connected with projectiles.

(1) Greatest height.

(a) To find the time.

At the moment of the greatest height, the vertical component vanishes :

$\therefore$ $\qquad$ $V \sin \alpha - gt = 0$ $\qquad$ (see § 159).

$\therefore$ $\qquad$ $t = \dfrac{V \sin \alpha}{g}.$

(b) To find the greatest height.

When a body is projected vertically upwards, h, the highest point, is given by :

$$v^2 = 2gh \quad . \quad . \quad . \quad (§ 99)$$

or $\qquad$ $h = \dfrac{v^2}{2g}.$

$\therefore$ At the greatest height of the projectile

$$h = \frac{V^2 \sin^2 \alpha}{2g}.$$

As a special case, when

$$\alpha = 45°.$$

Since $\quad \sin 45° = \dfrac{1}{\sqrt{2}}, \quad h = \dfrac{V^2}{4g}.$

(2) Time to describe the range.

As shown above, time to reach the greatest height is given by

$$t = \frac{V \sin \alpha}{g}.$$

But time for the whole flight must be twice this.

∴ for the whole range

$$t = \frac{2V \sin \alpha}{g}.$$

(3) To find the range.

The distance OB (Fig. 149) is called the range.

Let R represent the range.

Since the horizontal component is unchanged; in time t,

$$R = V \cos \alpha \times t.$$

But, for the complete range

$$t = \frac{2V \sin \alpha}{g} \quad (\textit{see above}).$$

$$\therefore \qquad R = V \cos \alpha \times \frac{2V \sin \alpha}{g}$$

$$= \frac{2V^2 \sin \alpha \cos \alpha}{g}$$

or $$R = \frac{V^2 \sin 2\alpha}{g},$$

since $\sin 2\alpha = 2 \sin \alpha \cos \alpha.$

(Trigonometry, p. 108.)

Maximum range for a given velocity of projection.
From the above

$$R = \frac{2V^2 \sin \alpha \cos \alpha}{g},$$

where R is the range.

Since $\qquad \sin \alpha = \cos (90° - \alpha)$
and $\qquad \cos \alpha = \sin (90° - \alpha).$

∴ The same values of R will be obtained whether the angle of projection is α or $90° - \alpha$.

For example, the range will be the same whether the angle of projection is 30° or 90° − 30°—*i.e.*, 60°.

Although the range will be the same for both angles, the time taken and the greatest height will be different. This is apparent from Fig. 150.

For the larger angle, $V \sin \alpha$, the vertical component will be greater than $V \cos \alpha$, the horizontal component, since $\sin \alpha$ increases when α increases. For the smaller value of α, $V \cos \alpha$ will be the greater, since $\cos \alpha$ decreases as α increases.

Maximum range.

Using the formula

$$R = \frac{V^2 \sin 2\alpha}{g}.$$

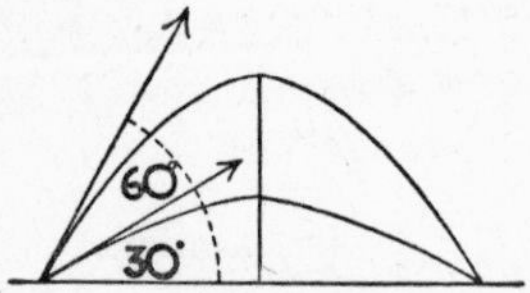

Fig. 150. 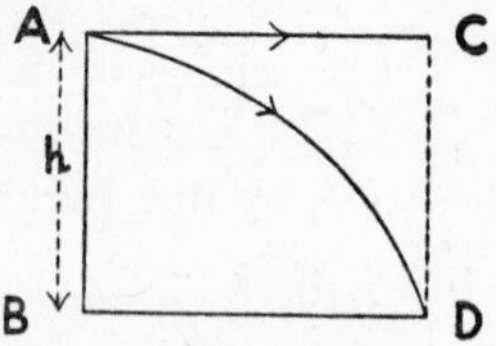   Fig. 151.

If V be constant, R is greatest when $\sin 2\alpha$ is greatest. But the maximum value of the sine of an angle is unity, when the angle is 90°.

∴ $\sin 2\alpha$ is greatest when $2\alpha = 90°$

and $\alpha = 45°$.

Then $R = \dfrac{V^2}{g}$.

When, therefore, in projecting a body, the maximum range is desired, as in throwing a cricket ball, the body should be projected at 45° to the horizontal.

161. Motion of a body projected horizontally from a height.

A familiar phenomenon of modern times is that of a body being dropped from an aeroplane, whether it be a package of food for the succour of marooned men, or a bomb intended for a more sinister purpose.

Suppose that, as shown in Fig. 151, a body is dropped from an aeroplane at A, a distance of h ft. above the ground, it being assumed the plane is flying horizontally.

Let V = velocity of the plane.

At the moment of projection the body projected will have the same velocity as the aeroplane—*i.e.*, V in a horizontal direction.

Therefore in their further motions the aeroplane will continue to move in a horizontal direction with velocity V, while the velocity of the bomb will have a horizontal component V. The bomb will also have a downward vertical velocity due to gravity, with an acceleration g.

∴ Time taken to reach the ground will be the same as if it fell from a height h.

The time of fall is given by the formula $h = \frac{1}{2}gt^2$.

∴ In time t given by this equation the bomb will have :

(1) fallen a distance represented by AB or CD.

(2) travelled a horizontal distance represented by AC, where

$$AC = V \times t.$$

∴ Its final position will be given by D, and the path described is a parabola.

Since the aeroplane also moves with a horizontal velocity V, in the same time t it will have travelled a distance equal to $V \times t$ and represented by AC. Thus it will have reached the point C, vertically above D, the position of the bomb.

This assumes that there is no air resistance affecting the motion of either body, but in practice, although this is not very considerable at low velocities, it is far from negligible at high velocities.

Both will also be affected by wind and air currents.

Summary of Formulae.

1. Components of velocity of projection.

　　Horizontal　　$V \cos \alpha$.
　　Vertical　　$V \sin \alpha$.

2. Height after time "t"

$$h = Vt \sin \alpha - \frac{1}{2}gt^2.$$

3. Time of flight $t = \dfrac{2V \sin \alpha}{g}.$

4. Horizontal range $R = \dfrac{V^2 \sin 2\alpha}{g}.$

5. Maximum range $R = \dfrac{V^2}{g}$

when $\alpha = 45°.$

6. Greatest height $h = \dfrac{V^2 \sin^2 \alpha}{2g}.$

163. Worked example.

The pilot of an aeroplane flying at a height of 16,000 ft., with a velocity of 180 m.p.h., aims at bombing a target directly in front of him. At what distance away, reckoned horizontally, must he release the bomb, if air resistance and air currents be ignored?

$$180 \text{ m.p.h.} = 180 \times \frac{22}{15} = 264 \text{ ft./sec.}$$

Time for bomb to fall from 16,000 ft. is found by using the formula $s = \frac{1}{2}gt^2.$
Substituting $16,000 = 16t^2.$

$\therefore$ $t^2 = 1,000.$

and $t = 10\sqrt{10} \text{ secs.}$

Distance travelled horizontally in this time is

$$(264 \times 10\sqrt{10}) \text{ ft.}$$
$$= \frac{264 \times 10\sqrt{10}}{5280} \text{ miles}$$
$$= \frac{\sqrt{10}}{2} = \frac{3 \cdot 1623}{2} = 1 \cdot 581 \text{ miles.}$$

$\therefore$ He must release the bomb at a distance of **1·58** miles (approx.), measured horizontally from the target.

Exercise 24.

1. A body was projected with a velocity of 80 ft./sec. at an elevation of 30° with the horizontal. Find its range and the greatest height which it reached.

2. Find the range of a gun when the muzzle velocity is 1200 ft./sec. and the elevation 24° 30′.

3. A target is 28,000 ft. from a gun and the muzzle velocity is 1200 ft./sec. What are the possible angles of projection?

4. A projectile has a muzzle velocity of 1520 ft./sec. What is its greatest range on a horizontal surface?

5. A projectile has a muzzle velocity of 1650 ft./sec. Find the range in yards on a horizontal plane if the angle of projection is 15°. Find the error at this range, due to an error of 15′ in the angle of elevation of the gun.

6. A stone is thrown up with a velocity of 100 ft./sec. at an angle of 45° with the horizontal. Find when and where it reaches the ground.

7. A cricket ball is thrown at an angle of 45° with the ground and pitches 100 yds. from the thrower, whose height above the ground (supposed horizontal) may be disregarded. With what velocity must the ball be thrown, and how high will it rise in the air?

8. A shot is fired with a muzzle velocity of 1200 ft./sec. and at an angle of 30° with the horizontal. How high is it after 5 secs.? Find (1) the greatest height which it reaches and (2) the horizontal range?

9. A stone is thrown in a horizontal direction with a velocity of 50 ft./sec. from the edge of a vertical cliff 80 ft. high. Determine the time which elapses before it reaches the ground and the distance measured horizontally of the point of impact from the point of projection?

10. An aeroplane travelling at a height of 1600 yds. above the ground at a uniform speed of 100 m.p.h. drops a bomb. Find (a) the time taken for the bomb to reach the ground, (b) the horizontal distance between the vertical lines through the point at which the bomb was released and the point at which it struck the ground, (c) the magnitude and direction of the velocity of the bomb on striking the ground. (Neglect air resistance.)

11. A boy stands 15 ft. away from a house and throws a ball so that it goes horizontally into a window 25 ft. above him and falls into the room. With what velocity and at what angle of elevation must he throw the ball?

CHAPTER XV

DENSITY; SPECIFIC GRAVITY

164. Density.

In § 103 it was stated that "mass is the quantity of matter" in a body. This "quantity" is measured by the effect of the force of gravity on it—*i.e.*, by its weight. Thus the mass is measured by its weight alone, without reference to its volume. But the volumes of a pound of lead and of a pound of sugar are very different; on the other hand, the weights of a cubic inch of lead and of a cubic inch of sugar are also very different.

But we frequently require to know the relation between the weights and volumes of various substances so that we may compare the weights of equal volumes of them.

In some substances the matter is said to be more dense than in others. We shall have a measure of this density if we know the weights of specified volumes, and it will clearly be an advantage if the specified volumes were standard units of volume such as a cubic inch, or a cubic foot, or a cubic centimetre. If therefore we know the weight of a cubic inch or cubic centimetre, we have a measure of the density of the substance.

Thus we arrive at the definition :

The density of a substance is the mass of a unit volume of it, and is measured by its weight.

In stating this density we may use one of two systems :

(1) The **foot-pound system** (F.P.S.), in which the cubic inch or cubic foot is the unit of volume and the pound is the unit of weight.

In this system the density of water is

62·3 lbs. per cubic foot, or
0·036 lb. per cubic inch.

(2) The **centimetre gram system** (C.G.S.), in which the unit of volume is the cubic centimetre and the gram is the unit of weight.

In this system the **density of water is**

1 gram per cubic centimetre.

The gram, the unit of weight in this system, is selected as being the weight of a cubic centimetre of water at 4° C.

Similarly :

Density of cast iron = 449 lbs. per cu. ft.
   ,,   lead   = 710 lbs. per cu. ft.

165. Relative density or specific gravity.

It is obviously an advantage if besides knowing the weights of unit volumes of various substances, we know the ratio of these to the weight of some suitable substance such as water.

If, for example, we know that the weight of a unit volume of iron is 7·2 times the weight of a unit volume water, it is a simple matter to calculate the weight of any volume of iron. Thus, the weight of 24·5 cu. ft. of iron would be 7·2 × 24·5 times the weight of a cu. ft. of water—*i.e.*, 62·3 lbs.

∴ The weight of the iron = (7·2 × 24·5 × 62·3) lbs.

It is natural that water should always be used for this comparison, and the ratio is called the **relative density** or **specific gravity** of the substance. It can be defined as follows:

The **relative density** or **specific gravity of a substance is the ratio of the weight of any volume of it to the weight of an equal volume of water.**

From this definition it will be observed that relative density is independent of the units employed, whether of weight or volume, as long as **equal volumes of each substance** are used and we know the weight of a unit volume of water.

Thus

$$\text{Relative density} = \frac{\text{density of the substance}}{\text{density of water}}$$

$$= \frac{\text{weight of substance}}{\text{weight of equal volume of water}}.$$

166. Determination of relative density.

(1) **Solids.** The only difficulty in the case of a solid is that of finding its exact volume, especially when the shape of it is irregular. A method of doing this will be given in a later chapter (§ 178).

The weight is found in the usual way by means of a balance. The rest is simple arithmetic. Examples will be given below.

(2) **Liquids.** A special bottle, called a **specific gravity bottle,** whose weight and interior volume are known, provides an easy way of finding the specific gravity of a liquid. Special precautions are taken to ensure that the volume of the liquid placed in the bottle is known exactly.

The bottle, full of liquid, is weighed, the weight of the bottle itself is subtracted, and thus the weight of the known volume of the liquid is found.

167. Worked examples.

Example 1. *Find the density and relative density of platinum when* 16 *cu. ins. weigh* 12·45 *lbs.*

Weight of 16 cu. in. $= 12 \cdot 45$ lbs.

$$,, \quad 1728 \quad ,, \quad = \frac{1728 \times 12 \cdot 45}{16}$$

$$= 1344 \cdot 6 \text{ lbs.}$$

∴ Density is 1344·6 lbs. per cu. ft.

But 1 cu. ft. of water weighs 62·3 lbs.

$$\therefore \quad \text{Relative density} = \frac{1344 \cdot 6}{62 \cdot 3}$$

$$= 21 \cdot 57.$$

Note.—It must be remembered that density is always expressed in weight per unit volume, whereas relative density being a ratio, is a number.

Example 2. *Find the weight of* 500 *yds. of copper wire of cross section* 0·085 *sq. in. when the S.G. of copper is* 8·82.

500 yds. $= 18,000$ ins.

Vol. of the copper $= (0 \cdot 085 \times 18,000)$ cu. ins.

$$= 1,530 \text{ cu. in.} = \frac{1,530}{1,728} \text{ cu. ft.}$$

Weight of 1 cu. ft. of water
$$= 62 \cdot 3 \text{ lbs.}$$
Weight of 1 cu. ft. of copper
$$= 62 \cdot 3 \times 8 \cdot 82 \text{ lbs.}$$

Weight of $\dfrac{1530}{1728}$ cu. ft. of copper

$$= 62 \cdot 3 \times 8 \cdot 82 \times \frac{1530}{1728}$$
$$= 486 \text{ lbs. (nearly).}$$

Exercise 25.

1. The volume of a piece of lead is 10·4 cu. in. and its weight is 4·193 lbs. What is the relative density of the lead?

2. Find the weight of 45·6 cu. in. of iron of relative density 7·3.

3. The specific gravity of an oil is 0·84. Find the volume of 2 tons of it, taking 1 cu. ft. of water to weigh 62·3 lbs.

4. If the relative densities of lead and iron are 11·2 and 7·8, respectively, find the difference in volume between one-half ton of each.

5. A sheet of plate-glass weighs 24 ozs. to the square foot. If the relative density of the glass is 2·5, what is the thickness of the glass?

6. A bottle contains 52 c.c. of mercury and weighs 752·2 gms. If the bottle weighs 45 gms., find the relative density of mercury.

CHAPTER XVI

LIQUID PRESSURE

168. Liquids and force.

In preceding chapters we have examined, from various aspects, the action of forces on solid bodies. These have been assumed to be rigid and to preserve their size and shape when acted upon by force. We must now consider briefly how forces act in relation to bodies which are not rigid—*i.e.*, fluids, which include liquids and gases. These have certain properties in common, but in this chapter we shall confine ourselves in the main to liquids, leaving the consideration of gases to a subsequent chapter.

A liquid, unlike a solid, offers very little resistance to a force which tends to change its shape. It yields to a thrust, and it is not possible for a force to act " at a point " on its surface. It does, however, resist any change in its volume by force. A perfect liquid is incompressible, but most liquids will allow a small change in volume under pressure.

169. Pressure of a liquid.

Since a force cannot act " at a point " of a liquid, as with a solid, different terms must be used when considering forces in relation to liquids and gases. For example, if a vessel contains liquid, the force of gravity acts on that liquid, and the " weight " of the liquid has to be borne by the base and sides of the vessel. We say that these are subjected to pressure.

To measure this, the area of the surface in contact with the liquid is divided by the total pressure on that surface. Thus is obtained the pressure per unit area.

If, for example, the area of the base of a vessel is 15

238

sq. in. and the total pressure on it is 200 lbs. wt., then the pressure on the base is described as being $\frac{200}{15}$ or $13\frac{1}{3}$ lbs. wt. per sq. inch.

Generally if area of surface = A sq. in.
and total pressure   = W lbs. wt.

then pressure on the surface = $\frac{W}{A}$ lbs. wt. per sq. in.

Again, when a force is applied to a liquid it must be done by means of a pressure on the surface of the liquid. Consider the example of a liquid in a syringe or in a cylindrical jar (Fig. 152). To apply a force to it we may use a piston which fits the vessel.

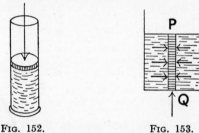

FIG. 152.   FIG. 153.

A force can be applied to this piston, and this in turn exerts a pressure on the whole of the free surface of the liquid. The force applied to the piston, divided by the area of its surface in contact with the liquid, gives the pressure per square unit which is applied to the surface of the liquid.

170. Pressure at a depth in a liquid.

When a vessel with vertical sides contains a liquid, the base is subject to a pressure due to the weight of the liquid above it, since this must be supported by the base.

In Fig. 153 let PQ represent a column of the liquid standing on unit area of the base.

This column is maintained in equilibrium by—

(1) Lateral pressures, from the surrounding liquid,

which are perpendicular to its surface, and therefore being horizontal have no vertical component.

(2) The weight of the liquid in the column.

(3) The upward thrust of the base.

The two latter must be equal and opposite.

Consequently **the pressure on the base**, being the sum of the weights of all such columns, **must be equal to the weight of the liquid.**

This **weight depends on the height of the column**, and upon the weight of a unit volume of the liquid, which in turn varies with the density of the liquid.

Pressure at any depth. Let any similar column of

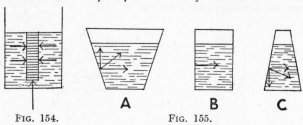

FIG. 154.   FIG. 155.

liquid be considered, as shown in Fig. 154. That is also maintained in equilibrium by :

(1) The lateral perpendicular pressures.

(2) The weight of the column.

(3) The upward pressure of the liquid on the base of the column.

This upward pressure must again be equal and opposite to the weight of the water in the column. But this is proportional to the height of the column. Therefore we arrive at the following conclusion :

The pressure at any point in a liquid is proportional to the depth below the surface of the liquid and to the density of the liquid.

This statement is true even when the sides of the vessel are not vertical. If vessels of different shapes but having the same area of base, as shown in Fig. 155, contain liquid to the **same depth** in each, the pressure on the base of each vessel is the same.

In (A) the pressure perpendicular to the surface of the side of the vessel has a vertical component which, acting upwards, supports the pressure of the extra amount of water. In (C) this pressure has a vertical component which acts downwards and increases the pressure on the base.

171. Transmission of pressure.

An important property of a fluid is that it transmits pressure equally in all directions. This can be demonstrated by means of the apparatus of which a cross-section is shown in Fig. 156. It consists of a vessel

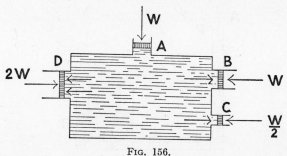

FIG. 156.

filled with water and with openings A, B, C, D, in which pistons are fixed. By means of these, additional pressures can be applied.

The openings at A and B are equal in area.

The area of C is half that of A, the opening of D is twice that of A.

All being in equilibrium, an additional pressure of W lbs. per sq. in. is applied to the piston at A. It is now found that to preserve equilibrium, additional pressures must be applied to the pistons at B, C, and D.

At B, with equal area to A, W lbs. wt. must be applied.

At C, with half the area of A, $\frac{W}{2}$ lbs. wt. must be applied.

At D with twice the area of A $2W$ lbs. wt. must be

I—MECH.

applied. Thus the pressure per sq. unit at A is applied equally to each square unit at the other pistons.

It can be concluded from such experiments that—

If a fluid is at rest, any change of pressure is transmitted equally throughout the fluid in all directions.

172. The hydraulic press.

The principle of transmissibility of pressure is applied practically in the **Hydraulic Press**. This is sometimes called the **Bramah Press**, from its inventor, a Yorkshireman named Joseph Bramah. The principle on which it is worked is shown in a simplified form in Fig. 157.

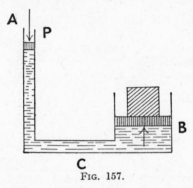

FIG. 157.

Two cylinders, A and B, of small and large cross-section areas respectively are connected by a tube C.

A piston called a plunger works down A, and another piston called the ram fits tightly into B; on top of this is placed the body which is to be subjected to pressure. Water is run into the machine as shown.

Let a pressure P be applied to the piston at A. This pressure, as explained in the preceding paragraph, is transmitted by the water equally to the whole of the area of the ram in B.

For example, let the area of A be 1 sq. in. and that of B be 40 sq. in.

Then when a pressure P is applied to A,

a pressure $40P$ is applied to B.

There is thus a mechanical advantage of 40 (*see* § 133).
This can be expressed generally as follows :
Let P = pressure applied to the plunger.
  ,, a = area of surface of plunger.
  ,, A = area of surface of ram.
Then pressure on the ram

$$= P \times \frac{A}{a}.$$

∴ Mechanical advantage

$$= \frac{A}{a}.$$

Frictional resistances have been neglected.

By increasing the area of the surface of the ram and
decreasing that of the plunger, great
pressures can be obtained.

The Hydraulic Jack is worked on the
same principle.

173. The Principle of Archimedes.

This famous principle can best be
illustrated by describing a simple experiment.

Experiment. Take a moderately
heavy object, preferably of regular
shape, such as a brick, and suspend it
from a spring balance. Note its weight.
Lower it carefully into a vessel containing water (*see* Fig. 158) until it is
completely covered. On reading the
balance again it will be found that it registers less weight
than before.

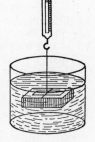

FIG. 158.

The brick has apparently lost weight. Let us consider
why this should be so, applying principles used previously.

Imagine the brick removed from the water and the
space it occupied filled again with water. This " block "
of water is in equilibrium, and the forces acting on it are :

> (1) The weight of the water acting vertically
> downwards.

> (2) The resultant upward thrust of the surround-
> ing water.

Since there is equilibrium, these must be equal and opposite.

∴ The upward vertical thrust of the surrounding water must be equal to the weight of the water which was displaced by the block.

∴ When the brick is in the water there are also two vertical forces acting on it :

(1) Its weight, say W, vertical, downwards.
(2) The upward thrust of the water, equal to the weight of the water displaced.

If w is the weight of the water displaced, the resultant downward thrust is

$$W - w.$$

This is the pull registered on the spring-balance. Or the pull registered is the weight of the brick less the weight of the water displaced.

The experiment may be repeated with other liquids of different densities, and the same result will be observed. The apparent weight of the brick will be equal to its real weight less the weight of the liquid displaced.

Thus we are able to formulate the theorem known as the **Principle of Archimedes.**

When a body is immersed in a liquid the upward pressure of the liquid on the body is equal to the weight of the liquid displaced.

The principle is so named because it was first discovered by the Greek mathematician, Archimedes, in the third century. The story of how it occurred to him as he lay in his bath is well known.

174. Specific gravity of a liquid by using the Principle of Archimedes.

It will probably occur to the student that this principle offers a method of finding the weight of a definite volume of the liquid. If a solid, not soluble in the liquid, and whose volume is known, is weighed in the liquid, as described in the above experiment, the apparent loss of weight of the body is equal to the weight of the liquid displaced. But this volume is equal to the known volume of the solid.

Knowing the weight and volume of the displaced liquid its specific gravity is readily determined.

This principle, and an experiment as above, can be used to find the volume of a solid, whatever its shape, regular or irregular. For this we need to know the specific gravity of the liquid.

For, if the solid be weighed (1) in air and (2) in the liquid, the difference in weight is the weight of the liquid displaced. If its specific gravity is known, we can find the volume of the water displaced, and this is the same as the volume of the solid.

175. Floating bodies.

Let a body of weight W be placed in a liquid.

Let w be the weight of the liquid displaced and therefore the upward thrust of the liquid.

Then the forces acting on the body are as shown in Fig. 159, both the forces being vertical in direction.

Considering the relative values of W and w, three cases may occur :

(1) If $W > w$ the body will sink.
(2) If $W < w$ the body will rise.
(3) If $W = w$ the body will rest in neutral equilibrium.

Fig. 159.

Considering the second case, viz. $W < w$, that is, when the upward thrust of the liquid displaced is greater than the weight of the body,

the body must rise.

When the body reaches the surface and emerges from the liquid, less of the body is immersed and less of the liquid is displaced.

Consequently w decreases.

But W remains constant.

As the body continues to rise, a time will come when

$$w = W.$$

I.e., the weight of the body is equal to the weight of the liquid displaced.

Then there will be equilibrium and the body will float.

Consequently: A body will float in a liquid when its weight is equal to the weight of the liquid which it displaces.

If a liquid of greater density is employed, w is increased and the body will float higher in the new liquid, while other bodies which would not float in the lighter liquid will now do so.

The general principle for a solid body is that it will float in a liquid of greater density than that of itself.

Thus iron, whose density is about 7·2, will float in mercury, whose density is 13·6.

176. If a body immersed in a liquid is hollow instead of being solid, it displaces more of the liquid. Consequently the upward thrust, equal to the weight of displaced water, is greater than the weight of the solid. That is the reason why a ship, though built of iron, being hollow, displaces sufficient water for the upward thrust to be greater than the weight of the iron hull.

When the weight and displacement of the ship are known, it can be estimated what weight of cargo can be placed in the hold of the ship so that it does not sink so low as to be in danger of capsizing in high seas.

It should be noted that the density of salt water is greater than that of fresh water; it varies between 1·025 and 1·028. Consequently when a ship moves from fresh river-water to salt water, the weight of the water displaced is greater, the upward thrust increases, and the ship rises in the water. This is important in estimating the weight of the cargo which the ship can carry without sinking below the Plimsoll safety line, as it is called.

177. The Hydrometer.

The fact that a body floating in a liquid will rise or fall as the density of the liquid is increased or decreased suggests a convenient method of quickly determining the density of a liquid.

If a narrow hollow cylinder, weighted at the bottom to keep it vertical, be placed in liquids of known densities, the heights reached on the cylinder can be marked. Thus a graduated scale can be constructed. When the cylinder is placed in a liquid of unknown density, the mark reached on the scale by the level of the liquid will indicate its density.

This is the principle of the instrument known as the **Hydrometer.** The actual shape of the ordinary hydrometer is shown in Fig. 160. The cylinder with the graduated scale is long and slender, and below it is a bulb filled with air to give buoyancy. Below this is a smaller bulb containing mercury to keep the instrument vertical. The density is shown by the point reached on the graduated scale by the level of the liquid.

This instrument is used in industry for the rapid determination of the densities of milk, spirits, beer, etc. These are variations of the instrument for special purposes, but the general principle of their construction is the same.

FIG. 160.

178. Worked Example.

A rectangular block of wood 8 cm. by 5 cm. by 4 cm. and of relative density 0·7, floats in a liquid, and it is calculated that 60 c.c. of the wood are above the surface of the liquid. Find the specific gravity of the liquid.

Volume of the wood = 160 c.c.

Weight of the wood = (160 × 0·7) grams.

Volume of wood above the liquid = 60 c.c.

∴   „   „   in   „   „   = 100 c.c.

∴ 100 c.c. of the liquid are displaced.

Let ρ = specific gravity of the liquid.

Then wt. of liquid displaced = 100 ρ grams.

But weight of liquid displaced
                = weight of the floating body.

∴ $100 \times \rho = 160 \times 0 \cdot 7.$

∴ $\rho = \dfrac{160 \times 0 \cdot 7}{100} = 1 \cdot 12.$

Exercise 26.

1. Find the pressure in grams per sq. cm. at a point 50 metres below the surface of sea-water of specific gravity 1·024.

2. A conical flask 15 cms. high whose base has a diameter of 10 cms. is completely filled with a liquid of specific gravity 1·6. Find the force exerted by the liquid on the base of the flask. $\pi = 3\cdot14$.

3. A piece of iron in the shape of a rectangular prism, which is 4 cms. × 5 cms. × 6 cms., is placed in a vessel containing mercury. If the specific gravity of the iron is 7·2, and that of the mercury 13·6, find the volume of the mercury displaced.

4. A piece of brass weighing 210 gms. is suspended in water. If the specific gravity of brass is 8·4, find the upward thrust on it. What would the thrust be if sea-water of density 1·024 were used?

5. A cube of iron of relative density 7·2 is suspended by a wire in oil of density 0·8. The edge of the cube is 6 ins. Find the tension in the wire.

6. A solid of relative density 2·4 weighs 14·2 gms. in water. What is its weight in air?

7. After discharging 100 tons of cargo, a ship rises 4 ins. out of the water. Find the cross-sectional area at the water line.

8. If the diameters of the pistons in a hydraulic press are 0·5 in. and 10 ins., and the smaller one is worked by a lever whose velocity ratio is 8, what is the theoretical advantage of the machine?

9. In a hydraulic press if the pistons are 2 ft. and 2 ins. in diameter, respectively, calculate the effort required to support a load of 10 cwt.

CHAPTER XVII

THE PRESSURE OF GASES

179. The pressure of the atmosphere.

It is a curious circumstance that many people find it difficult to realise that gases have weight and can exert pressure. It is curious because we live in a mixture of gases, the atmosphere, and the pressure of the atmosphere is all-pervading, the whole of our body within and without being adapted to it. It is not easy to realise that every square inch of the body is under a pressure of 14 lbs., and that, for example, if the palm of your hand has an area of about 15 sq. ins., it is subjected to a pressure of over 200 lbs. wt. The fact that this is unnoticed and that it involves no muscular effort, is due to the principle stated in § 167 that a fluid, which includes liquids and gases, transmits pressure equally in all directions. Consequently all parts of the body are subjected to the same pressure. If the palm of the hand is subjected to a pressure of 200 lbs. wt., so also is the back of it; there is always a counterbalancing pressure.

The atmosphere, like all gases, conforms to the law of fluids that pressure is proportional to depth below the surface. Now, we do not know exactly how high the atmosphere extends. It has been estimated at about 50 miles. Some put it higher, and there are indications from observations on the passage of meteorites, of the existence of a highly rarified atmosphere at a height of 200 miles.

At the earth's surface, therefore, there is a pressure due to the weight of a high column of gas. This pressure naturally diminishes if we ascend, and is different at different heights.

This external change of pressure, if made rapidly, has

harmful effects upon the human body, as the internal pressures do not so quickly adapt themselves to external changes. Aviators, and even mountain climbers, have to take special precautions to avoid harmful effects to the body resulting from quick changes in pressure.

180. Measurement of air pressure.

Many experiments may be employed for demonstrating the weight of the air and its pressure. It will be sufficient for our purpose if we examine that devised by Torricelli, a pupil of Galileo.

Torricelli's experiment.

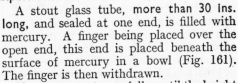

A stout glass tube, more than 30 ins. long, and sealed at one end, is filled with mercury. A finger being placed over the open end, this end is placed beneath the surface of mercury in a bowl (Fig. 161). The finger is then withdrawn.

The mercury at once falls, until the height of the column of mercury above the level of the mercury in the bowl is about 30 ins. or 76 cms.

The space which is thus left at the top of the column contains no air and is almost a perfect vacuum.

Let us consider why the column of mercury remains at this height. The forces acting on it are: (1) the force of gravity; (2) to balance this there must be an upward force, acting at the open end of the tube.

Fig. 161.

This upward force must clearly be due to the atmospheric pressure on the surface of the mercury in the bowl. This pressure is transmitted equally in all directions, and is therefore transmitted to the open end of the tube, as in the experiment described in § 171.

This atmospheric pressure must be sufficient to support the column of mercury.

The relative density of mercury is 13·6.

∴ The weight of a column of mercury 30 ins. high and a square inch in section is 14·7 lbs. (approx.).

Consequently the upward pressure at the free end of the tube is sufficient to support 14·7 lbs. of mercury to the square inch.

∴ The pressure of the atmosphere is 14·7 lbs. to the sq. in.

In the metric system this is approximately equal to 1020 gms. wt. per sq. cm.

If water had been used instead of mercury, since the relative density of mercury is 13·6, the column of water equivalent to the column of mercury would be

$$30 \times 13·6 = 408 \text{ ins. or } 34 \text{ ft. approx.}$$

It will be observed that the height of the column of the liquid is independent of the area of the cross-section of the tube.

181. Total pressure in a liquid.

In considering the pressure at varying depths in a liquid, as in the previous chapter, we have hitherto taken into account only the pressure due to the liquid itself. To obtain the **total pressure** at any depth we must add the atmospheric pressure, which acts on the surface of the liquid and is transmitted by the liquid, as in Torricelli's experiment.

182. The barometer.

The pressure of the atmosphere is not a fixed quantity, but varies within certain limits. As stated previously, it varies with the height above sea-level. It also varies with the weather. Generally speaking, the pressure increases in fine weather and decreases in wet and stormy weather. In consequence the column of mercury described in Torricelli's experiment will rise and fall.

To measure these changes in pressure the **barometer** ("pressure measurer") is employed.

This instrument consists, essentially, of a fine column of mercury, with the free end standing in a small reservoir of mercury, as in Torricelli's experiment.

A scale is fixed by the side of the top of the mercury on which may be read changes in the height of the column.

Adjustments have been devised, as in the modern Fortin barometer, to enable corrections to be made consequential on the fall of the mercury in the bowl, when the column of mercury rises, and conversely. There is also a vernier attachment which makes it possible to read changes in the height of the mercury to the nearest 0·01 of an inch.

The barometer is not only used to forecast changes in the weather, but it is essential in a large number of scientific experiments in which the atmospheric pressure is an important factor.

183. The aneroid barometer.

The long column of mercury essential to the barometer is inconvenient for many purposes, and we know of no heavier suitable liquid of which a shorter column would be sufficient. When, therefore, no very great accuracy is necessary, the **aneroid** barometer is used. In this instrument no liquid is employed (aneroid = without liquid).

It consists of an enclosed cylinder, from which the air has been partly exhausted, and having its sides made of thin metal, usually corrugated to provide a larger surface. Owing to the partial exhaustion of air, the pressure on the external surface of the box is greater than on the internal. Changes in the atmospheric pressure produce slight expansions or contractions in the surface of the box. These changes, which are very small, are conveyed by rods and magnified by a system of small levers. Ultimately they are registered by a pointer on a circular dial scale.

184. The siphon.

The pressure of the atmosphere is utilised in the siphon, an apparatus employed for the transfer of a liquid from one receptacle to another at a lower level. A bent tube ABC (Fig. 162) is filled with liquid and the ends are closed by the fingers. One end A is placed beneath the surface of the liquid which is to be transferred, and the other is put in position over the receptacle.

When the two ends are opened, the liquid will move

up the tube from A to B and then down to the receiving vessel.

To understand the reason for this, consider the pressures on a section of the water at B, the highest point of the tube.

Let P be the atmospheric pressure on the surface of the higher vessel. This is transmitted to the opening of the tube at A.

An equal pressure P also acts at C, the other end of the tube.

The other pressures are those due to the weight of the water in the two arms of the tube.

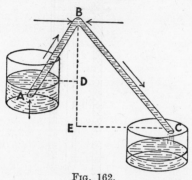

FIG. 162.

These are of different vertical heights, being :

    (1) BD for the *short* arm (D being the top of the surface in the vessel).

    (2) BE for the *long* arm.

But BE is greater than BD.

∴ Pressure on left side of $B = P -$ wt. of column BD of water.

And pressure on right side of $B = P -$ wt. of column BE of water.

∴ Pressure on left side is greater than the pressure on the right.

Consequently the water at B moves towards C.

And the atmospheric pressure at A continues to force water up the tube to B and thence to C.

185. Boyle's Law.

As has been stated in § 168, liquids are very slightly compressible, but gases change their volumes with changes in pressure and temperature. In this book, changes due to different pressures only will be examined.

As might be expected, the volumes of gases decrease when the pressure on them is increased, and conversely. The behaviour of gases under pressure was systematically

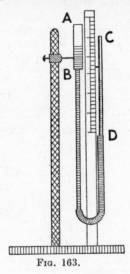

Fig. 163.

examined by Robert Boyle, who published the results of his experiments in 1661.

One of the discoveries he announced is the principle known as Boyle's Law. This can be demonstrated by means of the apparatus shown in Fig. 163.

A small amount of dried air is passed through mercury into a glass tube CD, closed at one end and clamped to a vertical scale on which the volume of the air may be read.

This tube is connected by means of a stout rubber tube with another vessel AB containing mercury. The height of the mercury in AB is also registered on a vertical scale. The vessel is open, and the surface of the mercury is consequently subject to atmospheric pressure.

The vessel AB can be moved up and down vertically.

Thus, the surface of the mercury being at different heights, different pressures due to the mercury are transmitted through the rubber tube to the mercury in the vessel CD, and so to the air above the mercury.

As AB is raised, the pressure on the air in CD is increased and the volume of air decreased.

When AB is lowered, the pressure on the air in CD decreases and the volume of the air increases.

A number of experiments are made at different pressures, and the corresponding volumes of the air are measured.

Let p be one of the pressures recorded.

Let v be the corresponding volume of air.

In each experiment the product $p \times v$ is calculated.

As a result of the experiments together with similar experiments on other gases it is found that *the product of p and v is constant.*

Thus $$p \times v = \text{constant.}$$

If k be the constant.

Then $$pv = k$$

$$\text{and} \quad p = \frac{k}{v}.$$

This is Boyle's Law.

It can be expressed as follows:

Boyle's Law. *The volume of a mass of gas is inversely proportional to the pressure on it.*

It is important to remember that the temperature must be kept constant throughout the experiments, and the law would more accurately be expressed thus :

If the temperature remains constant the volume of a mass of gas is inversely proportional to the pressure on it.

The actual compression of the gas is accompanied by a slight rise in temperature, and for accuracy the reading should not be taken until the temperature has fallen to its previous level.

Exercise 27.

1. When the height of the mercury in the barometer is 29·5 ins., what is the pressure of the atmosphere per sq. in. ? (Take the specific gravity of mercury as 13·6 and the weight of a cu. ft. of water as 62·3 lbs.)

2. If the height of mercury in a barometer is 30 ins., what would be the height if glycerine were employed instead of mercury? (Specific gravity of glycerine = 1·3.)

3. Find the total pressure at a point 16 ft. below the surface of a fresh-water lake, when the atmospheric pressure is 14·7 lbs. per sq. in.

4. What is the pressure in lbs. per sq. in. at a point 30 ft. below the surface of the sea, when the height of mercury in a barometer at the surface is 28·5 ins. ? (Specific gravity of mercury is 13·6; specific gravity of sea-water is 1·03; 1 cu. ft. of water weighs 62·5 lbs.)

5. The volume of a mass of gas is 50 cu. ins. when the height of the barometer is 29·4 ins. What will it be when the height is 30 ins. ?

6. A mass of gas has a volume of 500 c.c. when the pressure is equivalent to 76 cms. of mercury. What will be the volumes when the pressures are : (1) 125 cms. of mercury, (2) 50 cms. of mercury?

7. A glass cylinder contains 1000 c.c. of air at a pressure of 2 atmospheres, and air is slowly released until the pressure is 1½ atmospheres. What fraction of the air is released, and what volume does the released air occupy?

8. The volume of a barrel is 4 cu. ft. Air is pumped in so that the pressure is raised from 14·7 lbs. per sq. in. to 350 lbs. per sq. in. What is the volume of the air pumped in?

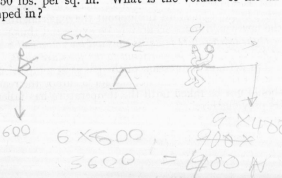

6ᴍ   9

600   9 × 400
6 × 600,   400 ×
3600 = 400 N

ANSWERS

p. 25.   Exercise 1.

1. (a) 6·4 ins. from C; 9·6 lbs. wt.
2. (a) $4\frac{8}{13}$ lbs.; (b) $10\frac{5}{13}$ lbs.; (c) 15 lbs.
3. $12\frac{1}{8}$ ins. from the centre.
4. (a) 4·2 ozs.; (b) 25·2 ins. from fulcrum.
5. $3\frac{1}{3}$ ozs.   6. 2·27 lbs.
7. $19\frac{1}{11}$ lbs.   8. (a) 3 lbs.; (b) 3·6 lbs.
9. $47\frac{1}{2}$ lbs.   10. 12 ins. from the weight of 5 lbs.

p. 33.   Exercise 2.

1. $5\frac{4}{7}$ lbs.; $4\frac{3}{7}$ lbs.
2. The stronger man 70·7 lbs.; the weaker 48·3 lbs.
3. $71\frac{2}{3}$ lbs.; $58\frac{1}{3}$ lbs.   4. 150 lbs. on C; 180 lbs. on D.
5. $86\frac{2}{3}$ lbs.; $113\frac{1}{3}$ lbs.   6. $7\frac{3}{4}$ lbs.; $5\frac{1}{4}$ lbs.
7. $\frac{1}{3}$ ton.   8. 141 lbs.; 57 lbs.

p. 42.   Exercise 3.

1. $4\frac{2}{7}$ lbs. wt.   2. $\frac{1}{8}$ ton wt.; $\frac{5}{8}$ ton wt.
3. $9\frac{1}{3}$ lbs. wt.; $1\frac{1}{3}$ lbs. wt.   4. 5 : 7 : 2.
5 $39\frac{1}{2}$ lbs. wt.   6. 56 lbs. wt.
7. 4 ft. from edge of cliff.   8. $53\frac{1}{4}$ lbs. per sq. in.
9. 240 lbs. wt.   10. 10 lbs. wt.

p. 57.   Exercise 4.

1. $3\frac{7}{8}$ ft. from A.   2. 3·7 ft. from A.
3. 3 ft. from A.   4. 8 lbs.
5. $\frac{4}{5}\sqrt{2}$ ft.
6. $\frac{2}{5}$ of the median from mid point of BC.
7. $4\frac{1}{12}$ ins. from O along OE, where O is the mid point of AD.
8. $2\frac{4}{5}$ ins. from the mid point of AB.
9. $1\frac{1}{4}$ ft. from OA; 1 ft. from OB.   10. $4\frac{2}{3}$ ins.
11. $\frac{1}{2} + \frac{1}{3}\sqrt{3}$ ins. from AB, or c.g. of equilateral triangle PQR.
12. $6\frac{1}{4}$ ins. from AB; 5 ins. from AD.

p. 64.   Exercise 5.

1. $4\frac{1}{8}$ ins.
2. $2\frac{1}{8}$ ins. from the lowest point of the hemisphere.
3. $1\frac{1}{3}$ ins. above the centre of the base.
4. $\frac{7}{80}$ in. from the centre.   5. $4\frac{1}{4}$ ins.; $3\frac{1}{2}$ ins.
6. 0·77 in. up the median from the uncut side.

257

7. (1) Neutral.
   (2) Stable for movement towards inside of table; unstable
       for movements away from table.
   (3) Stable.
   (4) Unstable, unless displacement very small.

p. 79.   Exercise 6.

1. (a) 26   (b) 27·5; 36° 52'.
   (c) 12·2.   (d) 8·71; 23° 25'.
   (e) 69° 35'.   (f) $\theta = 78° 28'$; $a = 44° 25'$.
2. (1) 5·83 lbs. wt.   (2) 30° 59'.
3. 11·63 lbs. wt.
4. (1) 20 lbs. wt.   (2) 19·32 lbs. wt.   (3) 18·48 lbs. wt.
   (4) 18·12 lbs. wt.   (5) 17·32 lbs. wt.   (6) 14·14 lbs. wt.
5. 60°   6. 120°.
7. 102·6 lbs. wt.   8. 18·03 lbs. wt.
9. BC in ratio 2 : 1; AC in ratio 3 : 1.

p. 87.   Exercise 7.

1. 13·9 lbs. wt.; 8 lbs. wt.   2. 10·88 lbs. wt.; 5·07 lbs. wt.
3. 4·59 lbs. wt.; 6·55 lbs. wt.   4. 19·1 tons wt.
5. (1) 15·3 lbs. wt.; 12·9 lbs. wt.
   (2) 216·5 grams wt.; 125 grams wt.
6. 376 lbs. wt.   7. 10·35 lbs. wt.
8. $\theta = 26° 34'$; 2 cwt.   9. 30·64 lbs.
10. 27·54 lbs. wt.

p. 96.   Exercise 8.

1. 17·84 lbs. wt.   2. 10·23 lbs. wt.; 81° 24'.
3. 10·15 lbs. wt.; 69° 49'.
4. 5·39 lbs. wt.; 23° 12' with OX in 4th quadrant.
5. 5·35 lbs. wt.; 85° approx. with OX in 1st quadrant.
6. 6 units along the 5th string.   7. 21 nearly; 57° nearly.
8. $2\sqrt{3}$ lbs. wt.; 30°.

p. 108.   Exercise 9.

1. 16⅔ lbs. wt.; 13⅓ lbs. wt.
2. $R = 18$ lbs. wt.; side opposite to $P = 2·5$ ins.
3. The second side is at right angles to the first; $14\sqrt{3}$ lbs. wt.;
   14 lbs. wt.
4. $P = 2·46$ lbs. wt. (approx.).   5. $P = 2·89$ lbs. wt. (approx.).
   $Q = 1·72$ lbs. wt. (approx.). $R = 5·77$ lbs. wt. (approx.).
6. $Q = 24·5$ lbs. wt.; $R = 27·3$ lbs. wt.
7. 9·2 lbs. wt.; 8·15 lbs. wt.
8. 12 tons wt. nearly; 6·01 tons wt.

p. 113.   Exercise 10.

1. $R = 15\frac{1}{2}$ lbs. wt. nearly; $\theta = 88\frac{1}{2}°$ nearly (calculated ans.
   11·98; 75° 54').
2. $R = 3·33$ lbs. wt.; $a = 70° 42'$.

3. 89 lbs. wt. 4. 10·2 lbs.; 38° 30′.

5. Resultant 3·2 lbs. wt. at 111° approx. to A; equilibriant equal to this in magnitude but opposite in direction.

6. 6 lbs.

p. 124. Exercise 11.

1. 0·42; 22° 47′. 2. 5·88 lbs. wt.
3. 3·84 lbs. wt. 4. 1·25 lbs. wt.
5. 42·8 lbs. 6. 1·88 lbs. wt.
7. (1) 8 lbs. wt. (2) 9·43 lbs. wt. (3) 7·84 lbs. wt.
9. 9·4 lbs. approx.

p. 128. Exercise 12.

1. (1) 0·404; (2) 1·87 lbs. wt. 2. 17° 13′.
3. (1) 39° 37′; (2) 21·8 lbs. wt. 4. 0·447.
5. 40 lbs. 6. 14·94 lbs. wt.
7. 55·8 lbs. wt. 8. 187 lbs. wt. nearly.

p. 144. Exercise 13.

1. (a) 100 ft./sec. (b) $68\frac{2}{11}$ m.p.h.
2. 352 ft. 3. 36 m.p.h.
4. 750 m.p.h. 5. 30 m.p.h.
6. 2·2 ft./sec. 7. $7\frac{1}{3}$; 25 m.p.h.
8. 7·5; 5; 0; − 12·5 (all in ft./sec.).
9. 120 m.p.h.; 60 m.p.h.; 48 m.p.h.; 36 m.p.h.; 24 m.p.h.; 12 m.p.h. 10. 115 ft.

p. 152. Exercise 14.

1. 40 ft./sec.; 160 ft. 2. 23 secs. nearly.
3. 22 secs.; 484 ft. 4. 1·1 ft./sec.²; 880 ft.
5. $3\frac{1}{5}$ ft./sec.²; $774\frac{2}{5}$ ft. 6. 3·91 ft./sec.²; $7\frac{1}{2}$ secs.
7. 1344 ft.

8. 38 ft. [Hint use formula $\dfrac{(u + v)}{2}$.]

9. 2·9 ft./sec.² 10. $91\frac{2}{3}$ ft.
11. $29\frac{1}{3}$ secs.; $645\frac{1}{3}$ ft. 12. 75 secs.
13. 10 secs. 14. $82\frac{1}{4}$ ft.; 5·6 secs. approx.

p. 157. Exercise 15.

2. 81 ft. 3. $3\frac{1}{3}$ secs.; $156\frac{1}{4}$ ft.
4. 400 ft.; 5 secs. 5. 80 ft./sec.; 100 ft.
6. 80 ft./sec.; 2·5 secs. 7. 112 ft.
8. $1\frac{1}{2}$ secs. ascending; $3\frac{1}{2}$ secs. descending.
9. 24 ft. 10. 48 ft./sec.; 1 sec. or 4 secs.
11. $6\frac{2}{11}$ ft./sec.²; $109\frac{4}{7}$ ft. 12. 31·89 metres; 5·1 secs.

p. 171. Exercise 16.

1. 12·8 ft./sec.² 2. 3 lbs. wt.
3. 64 lbs. wt. 4. $2\frac{3}{4}$ cwt. wt.
5. 0·88 ft./sec.² 6. 1050 lbs. (approx.).

7. $\frac{25}{60}$ lbs. wt.   8. 12 tons wt. (nearly).
9. 2304 lbs. wt.   10. $\frac{121}{441}$ tons wt.
11. (a) $6\frac{1}{8}$ lbs. wt. or between 6·1 and 6·2.   (b) 7 lbs. wt.
     (c) $7\frac{7}{16}$ lbs. wt., or between 7·4 and 7·5.
12. $5\frac{5}{8}$ lbs. wt.   13. 10 tons wt.
14. $194\frac{1}{4}$ lbs. wt.   15. $32\frac{1}{2}$ lbs. wt.

p. 177.   Exercise 17.

1. $\frac{10}{7}$ lbs. wt.; $9\frac{1}{2}$ ft./sec.².   2. $28\frac{4}{17}$ ft./sec.².

3. 4·8 lbs. wt.; 9·6 lbs. wt.   4. $28\frac{1}{4}$ ft.
6. 4·8 lbs. wt.; 6·4 ft./sec.².   5. 122·5 cm./sec.

p. 180.   Exercise 18.

1. 385 lbs. wt.   2. (a) $43\frac{3}{4}$ sec. lbs. wt.
         (b) $4\frac{3}{8}$ lbs. wt.
3. $18\frac{3}{4}$ lbs. wt.   4. $2\frac{1}{12}$ lbs. wt.
5. 64 ft./sec.; 48 sec. lbs. wt.   6. $1\frac{7}{8}$ lbs. wt.

p. 187.   Exercise 19.

1. (1) 1350 ft.-lbs.   (2) 33,880 ft.-lbs.
2. 9075 ft.-lbs.   3. 2500 ft.-lbs.
4. $564\frac{3}{8}$ lbs. wt.   5. $23\frac{7}{16}$ ft.
6. $4\frac{1}{2}$ lbs. wt.   7. $1512\frac{1}{2}$ ft.-lbs.
8. 100 ft.-lbs.; 100 ft.-lbs.   9. $10\frac{1}{12}$ tons.
10. $703\frac{1}{8}$ ft.-lbs.; $\frac{32}{48}$.   11. 2800 ft.-lbs.
12. 25 tons wt.

p. 190.   Exercise 20.

1. 268·8.   2. 11·2.
3. $7\frac{5}{15}$.   4. $\frac{7}{45}$.
5. $112\frac{1}{2}$ lbs.   6. 37,800.
7. 1800.   8. 1·91.
9. $\frac{7}{8}$.   10. 8·3.
11. 195·4.   12. $\frac{3}{25}$.

p. 211.   Exercise 21.

1. (a) $3\frac{1}{3}$;   (b) $3\frac{1}{8}$;   (c) 96%.
2. $71\frac{7}{9}$.   3. 125 lbs. wt.
4. $8\frac{1}{3}$ lbs. wt.   5. $13\frac{1}{3}$ lbs. wt.; $37\frac{1}{2}$.
6. 15 nearly.   7. 3·96 lbs. wt.
8. 88; 25·4%.
9. (a) 30 ft.-lbs.;   (b) 9 ft.-lbs.;   (c) 77%.
10. $E = 0.06W + 0.2$.   11. $E = 0.3W + 1.1$.
12. $E = 0.45W$.   13. $E = 0.09W + 3.5$.
14. $E = 0.4W + 3.5$.

p. 220.   Exercise 22.

1. (a) 17·44 ft./sec.; 23° 26′.
   (b) 20·7 m.p.h.; 21° 54′.
2. 15·3 m.p.h.; 11° 18′ with axis of ship.
3. 5·6 knots (approx.); 67° 35′ N. of W.
4. 1 hr. 9·3 mins.   5. 11° 51′ S. of E.; 103·4 m.p.h.
6. 98 m.p.h., and 11½° practically. By Trigonometry 97·98
   m.p.h. and 11° 32′.
7. 1 hr. 46 mins. (approx.).   8. 36 m.p.h.; 48 m.p.h.

p. 225.   Exercise 23.

1. 5 m.p.h.; 36° 52′ S. of E.
2. 20·3 m.p.h.; 47° 12′ N. of E.
3. 50 m.p.h.; 53° 8′ E. of N.
4. 67 m.p.h. (nearly); 63° 26′ N. of E.
5. 15 m.p.h.; 36° 52′ W. of N.; 6 miles.
6. 21·2 m.p.h.; 3° 16′ S. of W.
7. 28 knots; 27° S. of E.

p. 232.   Exercise 24.

1. 173 ft.; 25 ft.   2. 34,000 ft. nearly.
3. 19° 14′ or 70° 46′.   4. 72,200 ft.
5. 14,180 yds.; 217 yds. approx.   6. 4·42 secs.; 312½ ft.
7. 98 ft./sec. approx.; 75 ft.
8. 2600 ft.; 5625 ft.; 38,970 ft.
9. 2·24 secs. approx.; 137·5 ft.
10. 17·32 secs.; 2541 ft.; 573 ft./sec.; 75° 10′.
11. 41·8 ft./sec.; 73° 18′.

p. 237.   Exercise 25.

1. 11·19.   2. 12 lbs. approx.
3. 85·6 cu. ft. approx.   4. 0·7 cu. ft. nearly.
5. 0·116 in. approx.   6. 13·6.

p. 248.   Exercise 26.

1. 5120 gms. wt./sq. cm.   2. 1884 gms. wt. (approx.).
3. 63·53 c.c.   4. 25 gms. wt.; 25·6 gms. wt.
5. 49·84 lbs. wt.   6. 24·34 gms.
7. 10,750 sq. ft. (nearly).   8. 3200.
9. 7⅞ lbs. wt.

p. 256.   Exercise 27.

1. 14·46 lbs. per sq. in.   2. 313·8 ins.
3. 21·62 lbs. per sq. in.   4. 27·42 lbs. per sq. in.
5. 49 cu. in.   6. (1) 304 c.c.; 760 c.c.
7. ¼; 500 c.c.   8. 91 cu. ft. (nearly).

LOGARITHMS of numbers 100 to 549

	0	1	2	3	4	5	6	7	8	9	1	2	3	4	5	6	7	8	9
10	0000	0043	0086	0128	0170	0212	0253	0294	0334	0374	4	8	12	17	21	25	29	33	37
11	0414	0453	0492	0531	0569	0607	0645	0682	0719	0755	4	8	11	15	19	23	26	30	34
12	0792	0828	0864	0899	0934	0969	1004	1038	1072	1106	3	7	10	14	17	21	24	28	31
13	1139	1173	1206	1239	1271	1303	1335	1367	1399	1430	3	6	10	13	16	19	23	26	29
14	1461	1492	1523	1553	1584	1614	1644	1673	1703	1732	3	6	9	12	15	18	21	24	27
15	1761	1790	1818	1847	1875	1903	1931	1959	1987	2014	3	6	8	11	14	17	20	22	25
16	2041	2068	2095	2122	2148	2175	2201	2227	2253	2279	3	5	8	11	13	16	18	21	24
17	2304	2330	2355	2380	2405	2430	2455	2480	2504	2529	2	5	7	10	12	15	17	20	22
18	2553	2577	2601	2625	2648	2672	2695	2718	2742	2765	2	5	7	9	12	14	16	19	21
19	2788	2810	2833	2856	2878	2900	2923	2945	2967	2989	2	4	7	9	11	13	16	18	20
20	3010	3032	3054	3075	3096	3118	3139	3160	3181	3201	2	4	6	8	11	13	15	17	19
21	3222	3243	3263	3284	3304	3324	3345	3365	3385	3404	2	4	6	8	10	12	14	16	18
22	3424	3444	3464	3483	3502	3522	3541	3560	3579	3598	2	4	6	8	10	12	14	15	17
23	3617	3636	3655	3674	3692	3711	3729	3747	3766	3784	2	4	6	7	9	11	13	15	17
24	3802	3820	3838	3856	3874	3892	3909	3927	3945	3962	2	4	5	7	9	11	12	14	16
25	3979	3997	4014	4031	4048	4065	4082	4099	4116	4133	2	3	5	7	9	10	12	14	15
26	4150	4166	4183	4200	4216	4232	4249	4265	4281	4298	2	3	5	7	8	10	11	13	15
27	4314	4330	4346	4362	4378	4393	4409	4425	4440	4456	2	3	5	6	8	9	11	13	14
28	4472	4487	4502	4518	4533	4548	4564	4579	4594	4609	2	3	5	6	8	9	11	12	14
29	4624	4639	4654	4669	4683	4698	4713	4728	4742	4757	1	3	4	6	7	9	10	12	13
30	4771	4786	4800	4814	4829	4843	4857	4871	4886	4900	1	3	4	6	7	9	10	11	13
31	4914	4928	4942	4955	4969	4983	4997	5011	5024	5038	1	3	4	6	7	8	10	11	12
32	5051	5065	5079	5092	5105	5119	5132	5145	5159	5172	1	3	4	5	7	8	9	11	12
33	5185	5198	5211	5224	5237	5250	5263	5276	5289	5302	1	3	4	5	6	8	9	10	12
34	5315	5328	5340	5353	5366	5378	5391	5403	5416	5428	1	3	4	5	6	8	9	10	11
35	5441	5453	5465	5478	5490	5502	5514	5527	5539	5551	1	2	4	5	6	7	9	10	11
36	5563	5575	5587	5599	5611	5623	5635	5647	5658	5670	1	2	4	5	6	7	8	10	11
37	5682	5694	5705	5717	5729	5740	5752	5763	5775	5786	1	2	3	5	6	7	8	9	10
38	5798	5809	5821	5832	5843	5855	5866	5877	5888	5899	1	2	3	5	6	7	8	9	10
39	5911	5922	5933	5944	5955	5966	5977	5988	5999	6010	1	2	3	4	5	7	8	9	10
40	6021	6031	6042	6053	6064	6075	6085	6096	6107	6117	1	2	3	4	5	6	7	9	10
41	6128	6138	6149	6160	6170	6180	6191	6201	6212	6222	1	2	3	4	5	6	7	8	9
42	6232	6243	6253	6263	6274	6284	6294	6304	6314	6325	1	2	3	4	5	6	7	8	9
43	6335	6345	6355	6365	6375	6385	6395	6405	6415	6425	1	2	3	4	5	6	7	8	9
44	6435	6444	6454	6464	6474	6484	6493	6503	6513	6522	1	2	3	4	5	6	7	8	9
45	6532	6542	6551	6561	6571	6580	6590	6599	6609	6618	1	2	3	4	5	6	7	8	9
46	6628	6637	6646	6656	6665	6675	6684	6693	6702	6712	1	2	3	4	5	6	7	7	8
47	6721	6730	6739	6749	6758	6767	6776	6785	6794	6803	1	2	3	4	5	5	6	7	8
48	6812	6821	6830	6839	6848	6857	6866	6875	6884	6893	1	2	3	4	4	5	6	7	8
49	6902	6911	6920	6928	6937	6946	6955	6964	6972	6981	1	2	3	4	4	5	6	7	8
50	6990	6998	7007	7016	7024	7033	7042	7050	7059	7067	1	2	3	3	4	5	6	7	8
51	7076	7084	7093	7101	7110	7118	7126	7135	7143	7152	1	2	3	3	4	5	6	7	8
52	7160	7168	7177	7185	7193	7202	7210	7218	7226	7235	1	2	2	3	4	5	6	7	7
53	7243	7251	7259	7267	7275	7284	7292	7300	7308	7316	1	2	2	3	4	5	6	6	7
54	7324	7332	7340	7348	7356	7364	7372	7380	7388	7396	1	2	2	3	4	5	6	6	7
	0	1	2	3	4	5	6	7	8	9	1	2	3	4	5	6	7	8	9

Proportional Parts

	0	1	2	3	4	5	6	7	8	9	1	2	3	4	5	6	7	8	9
55	7404	7412	7419	7427	7435	7443	7451	7459	7466	7474	1	2	2	3	4	5	5	6	7
56	7482	7490	7497	7505	7513	7520	7528	7536	7543	7551	1	2	2	3	4	5	5	6	7
57	7559	7566	7574	7582	7589	7597	7604	7612	7619	7627	1	2	2	3	4	5	5	6	7
58	7634	7642	7649	7657	7664	7672	7679	7686	7694	7701	1	1	2	3	4	4	5	6	7
59	7709	7716	7723	7731	7738	7745	7752	7760	7767	7774	1	1	2	3	4	4	5	6	7
60	7782	7789	7796	7803	7810	7818	7825	7832	7839	7846	1	1	2	3	4	4	5	6	6
61	7853	7860	7868	7875	7882	7889	7896	7903	7910	7917	1	1	2	3	4	4	5	6	6
62	7924	7931	7938	7945	7952	7959	7966	7973	7980	7987	1	1	2	3	3	4	5	6	6
63	7993	8000	8007	8014	8021	8028	8035	8041	8048	8055	1	1	2	3	3	4	5	6	6
64	8062	8069	8075	8082	8089	8096	8102	8109	8116	8122	1	1	2	3	3	4	5	5	6
65	8129	8136	8142	8149	8156	8162	8169	8176	8182	8189	1	1	2	3	3	4	5	5	6
66	8195	8202	8209	8215	8222	8228	8235	8241	8248	8254	1	1	2	3	3	4	5	5	6
67	8261	8267	8274	8280	8287	8293	8299	8306	8312	8319	1	1	2	3	3	4	4	5	6
68	8325	8331	8338	8344	8351	8357	8363	8370	8376	8382	1	1	2	3	3	4	4	5	6
69	8388	8395	8401	8407	8414	8420	8426	8432	8439	8445	1	1	2	3	3	4	4	5	6
70	8451	8457	8463	8470	8476	8482	8488	8494	8500	8506	1	1	2	2	3	4	4	5	6
71	8513	8519	8525	8531	8537	8543	8549	8555	8561	8567	1	1	2	2	3	4	4	5	5
72	8573	8579	8585	8591	8597	8603	8609	8615	8621	8627	1	1	2	2	3	4	4	5	5
73	8633	8639	8645	8651	8657	8663	8669	8675	8681	8686	1	1	2	2	3	4	4	5	5
74	8692	8698	8704	8710	8716	8722	8727	8733	8739	8745	1	1	2	2	3	4	4	5	5
75	8751	8756	8762	8768	8774	8779	8785	8791	8797	8802	1	1	2	2	3	3	4	5	5
76	8808	8814	8820	8825	8831	8837	8842	8848	8854	8859	1	1	2	2	3	3	4	5	5
77	8865	8871	8876	8882	8887	8893	8899	8904	8910	8915	1	1	2	2	3	3	4	4	5
78	8921	8927	8932	8938	8943	8949	8954	8960	8965	8971	1	1	2	2	3	3	4	4	5
79	8976	8982	8987	8993	8998	9004	9009	9015	9020	9025	1	1	2	2	3	3	4	4	5
80	9031	9036	9042	9047	9053	9058	9063	9069	9074	9079	1	1	2	2	3	3	4	4	5
81	9085	9090	9096	9101	9106	9112	9117	9122	9128	9133	1	1	2	2	3	3	4	4	5
82	9138	9143	9149	9154	9159	9165	9170	9175	9180	9186	1	1	2	2	3	3	4	4	5
83	9191	9196	9201	9206	9212	9217	9222	9227	9232	9238	1	1	2	2	3	3	4	4	5
84	9243	9248	9253	9258	9263	9269	9274	9279	9284	9289	1	1	2	2	3	3	4	4	5
85	9294	9299	9304	9309	9315	9320	9325	9330	9335	9340	1	1	2	2	3	3	4	4	5
86	9345	9350	9355	9360	9365	9370	9375	9380	9385	9390	1	1	2	2	3	3	4	4	5
87	9395	9400	9405	9410	9415	9420	9425	9430	9435	9440	0	1	1	2	2	3	3	4	4
88	9445	9450	9455	9460	9465	9469	9474	9479	9484	9489	0	1	1	2	2	3	3	4	4
89	9494	9499	9504	9509	9513	9518	9523	9528	9533	9538	0	1	1	2	2	3	3	4	4
90	9542	9547	9552	9557	9562	9566	9571	9576	9581	9586	0	1	1	2	2	3	3	4	4
91	9590	9595	9600	9605	9609	9614	9619	9624	9628	9633	0	1	1	2	2	3	3	4	4
92	9638	9643	9647	9652	9657	9661	9666	9671	9675	9680	0	1	1	2	2	3	3	4	4
93	9685	9689	9694	9699	9703	9708	9713	9717	9722	9727	0	1	1	2	2	3	3	4	4
94	9731	9736	9741	9745	9750	9754	9759	9764	9768	9773	0	1	1	2	2	3	3	4	4
95	9777	9782	9786	9791	9795	9800	9805	9809	9814	9818	0	1	1	2	2	3	3	4	4
96	9823	9827	9832	9836	9841	9845	9850	9854	9859	9863	0	1	1	2	2	3	3	4	4
97	9868	9872	9877	9881	9886	9890	9894	9899	9903	9908	0	1	1	2	2	3	3	4	4
98	9912	9917	9921	9926	9930	9934	9939	9943	9948	9952	0	1	1	2	2	3	3	4	4
99	9956	9961	9965	9969	9974	9978	9983	9987	9991	9996	0	1	1	2	2	3	3	4	4
	0	1	2	3	4	5	6	7	8	9	1	2	3	4	5	6	7	8	9

Proportional Parts

	0	1	2	3	4	5	6	7	8	9	1	2	3	4	5	6	7	8	9
·00	1000	1002	1005	1007	1009	1012	1014	1016	1019	1021	0	0	1	1	1	1	2	2	2
·01	1023	1026	1028	1030	1033	1035	1038	1040	1042	1045	0	0	1	1	1	1	2	2	2
·02	1047	1050	1052	1054	1057	1059	1062	1064	1067	1069	0	0	1	1	1	1	2	2	2
·03	1072	1074	1076	1079	1081	1084	1086	1089	1091	1094	0	0	1	1	1	1	2	2	2
·04	1096	1099	1102	1104	1107	1109	1112	1114	1117	1119	0	1	1	1	1	2	2	2	2
·05	1122	1125	1127	1130	1132	1135	1138	1140	1143	1146	0	1	1	1	1	2	2	2	2
·06	1148	1151	1153	1156	1159	1161	1164	1167	1169	1172	0	1	1	1	1	2	2	2	2
·07	1175	1178	1180	1183	1186	1189	1191	1194	1197	1199	0	1	1	1	1	2	2	2	2
·08	1202	1205	1208	1211	1213	1216	1219	1222	1225	1227	0	1	1	1	1	2	2	2	3
·09	1230	1233	1236	1239	1242	1245	1247	1250	1253	1256	0	1	1	1	1	2	2	2	3
·10	1259	1262	1265	1268	1271	1274	1276	1279	1282	1285	0	1	1	1	1	2	2	2	3
·11	1288	1291	1294	1297	1300	1303	1306	1309	1312	1315	0	1	1	1	2	2	2	2	3
·12	1318	1321	1324	1327	1330	1334	1337	1340	1343	1346	0	1	1	1	2	2	2	3	3
·13	1349	1352	1355	1358	1361	1365	1368	1371	1374	1377	0	1	1	1	2	2	2	3	3
·14	1380	1384	1387	1390	1393	1396	1400	1403	1406	1409	0	1	1	1	2	2	2	3	3
·15	1413	1416	1419	1422	1426	1429	1432	1435	1439	1442	0	1	1	1	2	2	2	3	3
·16	1445	1449	1452	1455	1459	1462	1466	1469	1472	1476	0	1	1	1	2	2	2	3	3
·17	1479	1483	1486	1489	1493	1496	1500	1503	1507	1510	0	1	1	1	2	2	2	3	3
·18	1514	1517	1521	1524	1528	1531	1535	1538	1542	1545	0	1	1	1	2	2	2	3	3
·19	1549	1552	1556	1560	1563	1567	1570	1574	1578	1581	0	1	1	1	2	2	3	3	3
·20	1585	1589	1592	1596	1600	1603	1607	1611	1614	1618	0	1	1	1	2	2	3	3	3
·21	1622	1626	1629	1633	1637	1641	1644	1648	1652	1656	0	1	1	2	2	2	3	3	3
·22	1660	1663	1667	1671	1675	1679	1683	1687	1690	1694	0	1	1	2	2	2	3	3	3
·23	1698	1702	1706	1710	1714	1718	1722	1726	1730	1734	0	1	1	2	2	2	3	3	4
·24	1738	1742	1746	1750	1754	1758	1762	1766	1770	1774	0	1	1	2	2	2	3	3	4
·25	1778	1782	1786	1791	1795	1799	1803	1807	1811	1816	0	1	1	2	2	3	3	3	4
·26	1820	1824	1828	1832	1837	1841	1845	1849	1854	1858	0	1	1	2	2	3	3	3	4
·27	1862	1866	1871	1875	1879	1884	1888	1892	1897	1901	0	1	1	2	2	3	3	3	4
·28	1905	1910	1914	1919	1923	1928	1932	1936	1941	1945	0	1	1	2	2	3	3	4	4
·29	1950	1954	1959	1963	1968	1972	1977	1982	1986	1991	0	1	1	2	2	3	3	4	4
·30	1995	2000	2004	2009	2014	2018	2023	2028	2032	2037	0	1	1	2	2	3	3	4	4
·31	2042	2046	2051	2056	2061	2065	2070	2075	2080	2084	0	1	1	2	2	3	3	4	4
·32	2089	2094	2099	2104	2109	2113	2118	2123	2128	2133	0	1	1	2	2	3	3	4	4
·33	2138	2143	2148	2153	2158	2163	2168	2173	2178	2183	0	1	1	2	2	3	3	4	4
·34	2188	2193	2198	2203	2208	2213	2218	2223	2228	2234	1	1	2	2	3	3	4	4	5
·35	2239	2244	2249	2254	2259	2265	2270	2275	2280	2286	1	1	2	2	3	3	4	4	5
·36	2291	2296	2301	2307	2312	2317	2323	2328	2333	2339	1	1	2	2	3	3	4	4	5
·37	2344	2350	2355	2360	2366	2371	2377	2382	2388	2393	1	1	2	2	3	3	4	4	5
·38	2399	2404	2410	2415	2421	2427	2432	2438	2443	2449	1	1	2	2	3	3	4	4	5
·39	2455	2460	2466	2472	2477	2483	2489	2495	2500	2506	1	1	2	2	3	3	4	5	5
·40	2512	2518	2523	2529	2535	2541	2547	2553	2559	2564	1	1	2	2	3	3	4	5	5
·41	2570	2576	2582	2588	2594	2600	2606	2612	2618	2624	1	1	2	2	3	4	4	5	5
·42	2630	2636	2642	2648	2655	2661	2667	2673	2679	2685	1	1	2	2	3	4	4	5	6
·43	2692	2698	2704	2710	2716	2723	2729	2735	2742	2748	1	1	2	2	3	4	4	5	6
·44	2754	2761	2767	2773	2780	2786	2793	2799	2805	2812	1	1	2	3	3	4	4	5	6
·45	2818	2825	2831	2838	2844	2851	2858	2864	2871	2877	1	1	2	3	3	4	5	5	6
·46	2884	2891	2897	2904	2911	2917	2924	2931	2938	2944	1	1	2	3	3	4	5	5	6
·47	2951	2958	2965	2972	2979	2985	2992	2999	3006	3013	1	1	2	3	3	4	5	6	6
·48	3020	3027	3034	3041	3048	3055	3062	3069	3076	3083	1	1	2	3	4	4	5	6	6
·49	3090	3097	3105	3112	3119	3126	3133	3141	3148	3155	1	1	2	3	4	4	5	6	7
	0	1	2	3	4	5	6	7	8	9	1	2	3	4	5	6	7	8	9

ANTI-LOGARITHMS

Proportional Parts

	0	1	2	3	4	5	6	7	8	9	1	2	3	4	5	6	7	8	9
.50	3162	3170	3177	3184	3192	3199	3206	3214	3221	3228	1	1	2	3	4	4	5	6	7
.51	3236	3243	3251	3258	3266	3273	3281	3289	3296	3304	1	2	2	3	4	5	5	6	7
.52	3311	3319	3327	3334	3342	3350	3357	3365	3373	3381	1	2	2	3	4	5	5	6	7
.53	3388	3396	3404	3412	3420	3428	3436	3443	3451	3459	1	2	2	3	4	5	6	6	7
.54	3467	3475	3483	3491	3499	3508	3516	3524	3532	3540	1	2	2	3	4	5	6	6	7
.55	3548	3556	3565	3573	3581	3589	3597	3606	3614	3622	1	2	2	3	4	5	6	7	7
.56	3631	3639	3648	3656	3664	3673	3681	3690	3698	3707	1	2	3	3	4	5	6	7	8
.57	3715	3724	3733	3741	3750	3758	3767	3776	3784	3793	1	2	3	3	4	5	6	7	8
.58	3802	3811	3819	3828	3837	3846	3855	3864	3873	3882	1	2	3	4	4	5	6	7	8
.59	3890	3899	3908	3917	3926	3936	3945	3954	3963	3972	1	2	3	4	5	5	6	7	8
.60	3981	3990	3999	4009	4018	4027	4036	4046	4055	4064	1	2	3	4	5	6	7	7	8
.61	4074	4083	4093	4102	4111	4121	4130	4140	4150	4159	1	2	3	4	5	6	7	8	9
.62	4169	4178	4188	4198	4207	4217	4227	4236	4246	4256	1	2	3	4	5	6	7	8	9
.63	4266	4276	4285	4295	4305	4315	4325	4335	4345	4355	1	2	3	4	5	6	7	8	9
.64	4365	4375	4385	4395	4406	4416	4426	4436	4446	4457	1	2	3	4	5	6	7	8	9
.65	4467	4477	4487	4498	4508	4519	4529	4539	4550	4560	1	2	3	4	5	6	7	8	9
.66	4571	4581	4592	4603	4613	4624	4634	4645	4656	4667	1	2	3	4	5	6	7	8	10
.67	4677	4688	4699	4710	4721	4732	4742	4753	4764	4775	1	2	3	4	5	7	8	9	10
.68	4786	4797	4808	4819	4831	4842	4853	4864	4875	4887	1	2	3	4	6	7	8	9	10
.69	4898	4909	4920	4932	4943	4955	4966	4977	4989	5000	1	2	3	5	6	7	8	9	10
.70	5012	5023	5035	5047	5058	5070	5082	5093	5105	5117	1	2	4	5	6	7	8	9	11
.71	5129	5140	5152	5164	5176	5188	5200	5212	5224	5236	1	2	4	5	6	7	8	10	11
.72	5248	5260	5272	5284	5297	5309	5321	5333	5346	5358	1	2	4	5	6	7	9	10	11
.73	5370	5383	5395	5408	5420	5433	5445	5458	5470	5483	1	3	4	5	6	8	9	10	11
.74	5495	5508	5521	5534	5546	5559	5572	5585	5598	5610	1	3	4	5	6	8	9	10	12
.75	5623	5636	5649	5662	5675	5689	5702	5715	5728	5741	1	3	4	5	7	8	9	10	12
.76	5754	5768	5781	5794	5808	5821	5834	5848	5861	5875	1	3	4	5	7	8	9	11	12
.77	5888	5902	5916	5929	5943	5957	5970	5984	5998	6012	1	3	4	6	7	8	10	11	12
.78	6026	6039	6053	6067	6081	6095	6109	6124	6138	6152	1	3	4	6	7	8	10	11	13
.79	6166	6180	6194	6209	6223	6237	6252	6266	6281	6295	1	3	4	6	7	9	10	12	13
.80	6310	6324	6339	6353	6368	6383	6397	6412	6427	6442	1	3	4	6	7	9	10	12	13
.81	6457	6471	6486	6501	6516	6531	6546	6561	6577	6592	2	3	5	6	8	9	11	12	14
.82	6607	6622	6637	6653	6668	6683	6699	6714	6730	6745	2	3	5	6	8	9	11	12	14
.83	6761	6776	6792	6808	6823	6839	6855	6871	6887	6902	2	3	5	6	8	9	11	13	14
.84	6918	6934	6950	6966	6982	6998	7015	7031	7047	7063	2	3	5	6	8	10	11	13	14
.85	7079	7096	7112	7129	7145	7161	7178	7194	7211	7228	2	3	5	7	8	10	12	13	15
.86	7244	7261	7278	7295	7311	7328	7345	7362	7379	7396	2	3	5	7	8	10	12	14	15
.87	7413	7430	7447	7464	7482	7499	7516	7534	7551	7568	2	3	5	7	9	10	12	14	16
.88	7586	7603	7621	7638	7656	7674	7691	7709	7727	7745	2	4	5	7	9	11	12	14	16
.89	7762	7780	7798	7816	7834	7852	7870	7889	7907	7925	2	4	5	7	9	11	13	14	16
.90	7943	7962	7980	7998	8017	8035	8054	8072	8091	8110	2	4	6	7	9	11	13	15	17
.91	8128	8147	8166	8185	8204	8222	8241	8260	8279	8299	2	4	6	8	10	11	13	15	17
.92	8318	8337	8356	8375	8395	8414	8433	8453	8472	8492	2	4	6	8	10	12	14	15	17
.93	8511	8531	8551	8570	8590	8610	8630	8650	8670	8690	2	4	6	8	10	12	14	16	18
.94	8710	8730	8750	8770	8790	8810	8831	8851	8872	8892	2	4	6	8	10	12	14	16	18
.95	8913	8933	8954	8974	8995	9016	9036	9057	9078	9099	2	4	6	8	10	12	14	17	19
.96	9120	9141	9162	9183	9204	9226	9247	9268	9290	9311	2	4	6	8	11	13	15	17	19
.97	9333	9354	9376	9397	9419	9441	9462	9484	9506	9528	2	4	7	9	11	13	15	17	20
.98	9550	9572	9594	9616	9638	9661	9683	9705	9727	9750	2	4	7	9	11	13	16	18	20
.99	9772	9795	9817	9840	9863	9886	9908	9931	9954	9977	2	5	7	9	11	14	16	18	21
	0	1	2	3	4	5	6	7	8	9	1	2	3	4	5	6	7	8	9

NATURAL SINES

	0'	6'	12'	18'	24'	30'	36'	42'	48'	54'	1'	2'	3'	4'	5'
0°	0·0000	·0017	·0035	·0052	0070	0087	·0105	·0122	·0140	·0157	3	6	9	12	15
1	0·0175	·0192	·0209	·0227	0244	·0262	·0279	·0297	·0314	·0332	3	6	9	12	15
2	0·0349	·0366	0384	0401	0419	0436	·0454	·0471	0489	·0506	3	6	9	12	15
3	0·0523	·0541	·0558	·0576	0593	·0610	0628	·0645	·0663	·0680	3	6	9	12	15
4	0 0698	·0715	·0732	·0750	0767	·0785	·0802	·0819	·0837	·0854	3	6	9	12	14
5	0 0872	0889	0906	0924	0941	·0958	0976	0993	·1011	·1028	3	6	9	12	14
6	0 1045	1063	·1080	·1097	·1115	·1132	·1149	·1167	·1184	·1201	3	6	9	12	14
7	0·1219	·1236	·1253	1271	·1288	1305	·1323	·1340	·1357	·1374	3	6	9	12	14
8	0·1392	1409	·1426	·1444	·1461	·1478	·1495	·1513	·1530	·1547	3	6	9	11	14
9	0·1564	1582	·1599	·1616	1633	·1650	·1668	·1685	·1702	1719	3	6	9	11	14
10	0·1736	·1754	·1771	·1788	·1805	·1822	1840	·1857	·1874	·1891	3	6	9	11	14
11	0·1908	·1925	1942	·1959	·1977	1994	2011	·2028	2045	·2062	3	6	9	11	14
12	0 2079	·2096	2113	2130	·2147	·2164	2181	·2198	2215	·2232	3	6	9	11	14
13	0 2250	·2267	·2284	·2300	2317	·2334	2351	·2368	·2385	·2402	3	6	8	11	14
14	0·2419	·2436	·2453	·2470	·2487	2504	·2521	2538	·2554	·2571	3	6	8	11	14
15	0·2588	·2605	·2622	·2639	2656	2672	2689	·2706	·2723	·2740	3	6	8	11	14
16	0·2756	·2773	2790	2807	2823	·2840	2857	·2874	2890	·2907	3	6	8	11	14
17	0·2924	2940	2957	·2974	2990	3007	3024	3040	·3057	3074	3	6	8	11	14
18	0·3090	·3107	·3123	·3140	3156	·3173	·3190	·3206	·3223	·3239	3	6	8	11	14
19	0 3256	·3272	·3289	3305	3322	3338	3355	·3371	·3387	3404	3	5	8	11	14
20	0 3420	·3437	·3453	3469	3486	3502	3518	·3535	·3551	3567	3	5	8	11	14
21	0 3584	·3600	3616	3633	3649	3665	3681	·3697	3714	3730	3	5	8	11	14
22	0 3746	·3762	·3778	3795	3811	3827	3843	·3859	3875	3891	3	5	8	11	13
23	0·3907	·3923	·3939	3955	3971	3987	4003	·4019	4035	·4051	3	5	8	11	13
24	0·4067	·4083	·4099	4115	4131	4147	4163	·4179	4195	·4210	3	5	8	11	13
25	0·4226	·4242	4258	·4274	4289	4305	4321	·4337	·4352	4368	3	5	8	11	13
26	0 4384	4399	4415	·4431	4446	·4462	4478	·4493	·4509	·4524	3	5	8	10	13
27	0 4540	·4555	·4571	·4586	4602	·4617	4633	·4648	·4664	·4679	3	5	8	10	13
28	0 4695	·4710	·4726	4741	4756	·4772	4787	·4802	·4818	·4833	3	5	8	10	13
29	0·4848	·4863	·4879	·4894	4909	4924	4939	·4955	4970	·4985	3	5	8	10	13
30	0 5000	·5015	·5030	·5045	·5060	5075	5090	·5105	·5120	·5135	2	5	8	10	12
31	0·5150	·5165	·5180	5195	5210	·5225	5240	·5255	·5270	·5284	2	5	7	10	12
32	0·5299	·5314	·5329	·5344	·5358	·5373	5388	5402	·5417	·5432	2	5	7	10	12
33	0·5446	·5461	·5476	5490	5505	·5519	5534	·5548	·5563	·5577	2	5	7	10	12
34	0·5592	·5606	·5621	5635	5650	·5664	5678	·5693	·5707	·5721	2	5	7	10	12
35	0·5736	·5750	·5764	5779	·5793	·5807	·5821	·5835	·5850	·5864	2	5	7	9	12
36	0·5878	·5892	·5906	5920	5934	·5948	·5962	·5976	·5990	·6004	2	5	7	9	12
37	0·6018	·6032	·6046	·6060	·6074	6088	·6101	·6115	·6129	·6143	2	5	7	9	12
38	0·6157	·6170	·6184	·6198	·6211	·6225	·6239	·6252	·6266	·6280	2	5	7	9	11
39	0·6293	·6307	·6320	·6334	6347	·6361	·6374	·6388	·6401	·6414	2	4	7	9	11
40	0·6428	·6441	·6455	·6468	6481	·6494	·6508	·6521	·6534	·6547	2	4	7	9	11
41	0·6561	·6574	·6587	·6600	6613	·6626	·6639	·6652	·6665	·6678	2	4	6	9	11
42	0·6691	·6704	·6717	·6730	6743	·6756	·6769	·6782	·6794	·6807	2	4	6	9	11
43	0·6820	·6833	·6845	·6858	·6871	·6884	·6896	·6909	·6921	·6934	2	4	6	8	11
44	0·6947	·6959	·6972	·6984	·6997	·7009	·7022	·7034	·7046	·7059	2	4	6	8	10
	0'	6'	12'	18'	24'	30'	36'	42'	48'	54'	1'	2'	3'	4'	5'

NATURAL SINES

	0'	6'	12'	18'	24'	30'	36'	42'	48'	54'	1'	2'	3'	4'	5'
45°	0·7071	·7083	·7096	·7108	·7120	·7133	·7145	·7157	·7169	·7181	2	4	6	8	10
46	0·7193	·7206	·7218	·7230	·7242	·7254	·7266	·7278	·7290	·7302	2	4	6	8	10
47	0·7314	·7325	·7337	·7349	·7361	·7373	·7385	·7396	·7408	·7420	2	4	6	8	10
48	0·7431	·7443	·7455	·7466	·7478	·7490	·7501	·7513	·7524	·7536	2	4	6	8	10
49	0·7547	·7559	·7570	·7581	·7593	·7604	·7615	·7627	·7638	·7649	2	4	6	8	9
50	0·7660	·7672	·7683	·7694	·7705	·7716	·7727	·7738	·7749	·7760	2	4	6	7	9
51	0·7771	·7782	·7793	·7804	·7815	·7826	·7837	·7848	·7859	·7869	2	4	5	7	9
52	0·7880	·7891	·7902	·7912	·7923	·7934	·7944	7955	·7965	·7976	2	4	5	7	9
53	0·7986	·7997	·8007	·8018	·8028	·8039	·8049	·8059	·8070	8080	2	3	5	7	9
54	0·8090	·8100	·8111	·8121	·8131	8141	·8151	8161	·8171	·8181	2	3	5	7	8
55	0·8192	·8202	·8211	·8221	·8231	8241	·8251	8261	·8271	·8281	2	3	5	7	8
56	0·8290	·8300	·8310	·8320	8329	·8339	·8348	·8358	·8368	·8377	2	3	5	6	8
57	0·8387	·8396	·8406	·8415	·8425	·8434	·8443	·8453	·8462	·8471	2	3	5	6	8
58	0·8480	·8490	·8499	·8508	·8517	·8526	·8536	·8545	·8554	·8563	2	3	5	6	8
59	0·8572	·8581	·8590	·8599	8607	·8616	8625	8634	8643	8652	1	3	4	6	7
60	0·8660	·8669	·8678	·8686	8695	8704	8712	8721	8729	8738	1	3	4	6	7
61	0·8746	·8755	·8763	·8771	8780	8788	8796	·8805	·8813	·8821	1	3	4	6	7
62	0·8829	·8838	·8846	·8854	8862	8870	8878	8886	·8894	·8902	1	3	4	5	7
63	0·8910	·8918	8926	·8934	8942	8949	8957	8965	8973	8980	1	3	4	5	6
64	0·8988	·8996	·9003	·9011	9018	9026	9033	9041	9048	9056	1	2	4	5	6
65	0·9063	·9070	·9078	9085	9092	9100	·9107	9114	9121	9128	1	2	4	5	6
66	0·9135	·9143	·9150	·9157	·9164	9171	·9178	·9184	·9191	9198	1	2	3	5	6
67	0·9205	·9212	·9219	·9225	·9232	·9239	9245	9252	9259	·9265	1	2	3	4	6
68	0·9272	·9278	·9285	·9291	·9298	9304	9311	9317	9323	9330	1	2	3	4	5
69	0·9336	·9342	·9348	·9354	·9361	9367	9373	9379	9385	9391	1	2	3	4	5
70	0·9397	·9403	·9409	·9415	·9421	9426	9432	9438	9444	9449	1	2	3	4	5
71	0·9455	·9461	·9466	·9472	·9478	9483	9489	9494	9500	9505	1	2	3	4	5
72	0·9511	·9516	·9521	·9527	·9532	9537	9542	·9548	9553	9558	1	2	3	3	4
73	0·9563	·9568	·9573	·9578	·9583	9588	9593	9598	9603	9608	1	2	2	3	4
74	0·9613	·9617	·9622	·9627	9632	9636	9641	9646	9650	9655	1	2	2	3	4
75	0·9659	·9664	·9668	·9673	·9677	9681	9686	·9690	9694	9699	1	1	2	3	4
76	0·9703	·9707	·9711	·9715	9720	9724	9728	9732	9736	9740	1	1	2	3	3
77	0·9744	·9748	·9751	·9755	·9759	·9763	·9767	·9770	·9774	·9778	1	1	2	2	3
78	0·9781	·9785	·9789	·9792	·9796	·9799	·9803	·9806	·9810	·9813	1	1	2	2	3
79	0·9816	·9820	·9823	·9826	9829	·9833	·9836	·9839	·9842	·9845	1	1	2	2	3
80	0·9848	·9851	·9854	·9857	9860	9863	9866	9869	9871	9874	0	1	1	2	2
81	0·9877	·9880	·9882	9885	9888	·9890	9893	9895	·9898	9900	0	1	1	2	2
82	0·9903	·9905	·9907	9910	·9912	9914	9917	9919	·9921	·9923	0	1	1	1	2
83	0·9925	·9928	·9930	·9932	·9934	·9936	9938	9940	9942	9943	0	1	1	1	2
84	0·9945	·9947	·9949	9951	·9952	·9954	9956	9957	·9959	9960	0	1	1	1	1
85	0·9962	·9963	9965	·9966	9968	9969	9971	9972	9973	9974	0	0	1	1	1
86	0·9976	·9977	·9978	·9979	9980	·9981	9982	9983	9984	9985	0	0	0	1	1
87	0·9986	·9987	9988	·9989	9990	·9990	9991	9992	·9993	9993	0	0	0	1	1
88	0·9994	·9995	·9995	9996	9996	9997	9997	9997	9998	9998	0	0	0	0	0
89	0·9998	·9999	·9999	·9999	0·9999	1·0000	0000	0000	0000	0000	0	0	0	0	0
	0'	6'	12'	18'	24'	30'	36'	42'	48'	54'	1'	2'	3'	4'	5'

NATURAL COSINES

	0	6'	12'	18'	24'	30'	36'	42'	48'	54'	1'	2'	3'	4'	5'
0°	1 0000	0000	0000	·0000	·0000	1·0000	0 9999	·9999	·9999	·9999	0	0	0	0	0
1	0 9998	9998	9998	·9997	·9997	·9997	·9996	·9996	·9995	·9995	0	0	0	0	0
2	0 9994	9993	9993	9992	9991	·9990	·9990	·9989	·9988	·9987	0	0	0	0	1
3	0 9986	9985	9984	9983	9981	·9980	·9979	·9978	·9977	·9977	0	0	0	1	1
4	0 9976	9974	9973	9972	9971	·9969	·9968	·9966	·9965	·9963	0	0	1	1	1
5	0 9962	9960	9959	9957	9956	·9954	·9952	·9951	·9949	9947	0	1	1	1	1
6	0 9945	9943	9942	9940	9938	·9936	·9934	·9932	·9930	·9928	0	1	1	1	2
7	0 9925	9923	9921	9919	9917	·9914	·9912	·9910	·9907	·9905	0	1	1	1	2
8	0 9903	9900	9898	9895	9893	·9890	·9888	·9885	·9882	·9880	0	1	1	2	2
9	0 9877	9874	9871	9869	9866	·9863	·9860	·9857	·9854	·9851	0	1	1	2	2
10	0·9848	·9845	·9842	·9839	·9836	·9833	·9829	·9826	·9823	·9820	1	1	2	2	3
11	0·9816	·9813	·9810	9806	·9803	·9799	·9796	·9792	·9789	·9785	1	1	2	2	3
12	0·9781	·9778	·9774	·9770	·9767	·9763	·9759	·9755	·9751	·9748	1	1	2	2	3
13	0 9744	·9740	·9736	·9732	·9728	·9724	·9720	·9715	·9711	·9707	1	1	2	3	3
14	0·9703	·9699	·9694	·9690	·9686	·9681	·9677	·9673	·9668	·9664	1	1	2	3	4
15	0 9659	·9655	·9650	·9646	·9641	·9636	·9632	·9627	·9622	·9617	1	2	2	3	4
16	0·9613	·9608	·9603	·9598	·9593	·9588	·9583	·9578	·9573	·9568	1	2	2	3	4
17	0·9563	·9558	·9553	·9548	·9542	·9537	·9532	·9527	·9521	·9516	1	2	3	3	4
18	0·9511	·9505	·9500	·9494	·9489	·9483	·9478	·9472	·9466	·9461	1	2	3	4	5
19	0·9455	·9449	·9444	·9438	·9432	·9426	·9421	·9415	·9409	·9403	1	2	3	4	5
20	0·9397	·9391	·9385	·9379	·9373	·9367	·9361	·9354	·9348	·9342	1	2	3	4	5
21	0·9336	·9330	·9323	·9317	·9311	·9304	·9298	·9291	·9285	·9278	1	2	3	4	5
22	0·9272	·9265	·9259	·9252	·9245	·9239	·9232	·9225	·9219	·9212	1	2	3	4	6
23	0·9205	·9198	·9191	·9184	·9178	·9171	·9164	·9157	·9150	·9143	1	2	3	5	6
24	0·9135	·9128	·9121	·9114	·9107	·9100	·9092	·9085	·9078	·9070	1	2	4	5	6
25	0·9063	·9056	·9048	·9041	·9033	·9026	·9018	·9011	·9003	·8996	1	2	4	5	6
26	0·8988	·8980	·8973	·8965	·8957	·8949	·8942	·8934	·8926	·8918	1	3	4	5	6
27	0·8910	·8902	·8894	·8886	·8878	·8870	·8862	·8854	·8846	·8838	1	3	4	5	7
28	0·8829	·8821	·8813	·8805	·8796	·8788	·8780	·8771	·8763	·8755	1	3	4	6	7
29	0·8746	·8738	·8729	·8721	·8712	·8704	·8695	·8686	·8678	·8669	1	3	4	6	7
30	0·8660	·8652	·8643	·8634	·8625	·8616	·8607	·8599	·8590	·8581	1	3	4	6	7
31	0·8572	·8563	·8554	·8545	·8536	·8526	·8517	·8508	·8499	·8490	2	3	5	6	8
32	0·8480	·8471	·8462	·8453	·8443	·8434	·8425	·8415	·8406	·8396	2	3	5	6	8
33	0·8387	·8377	·8368	·8358	·8348	·8339	·8329	·8320	·8310	·8300	2	3	5	6	8
34	0·8290	·8281	·8271	·8261	·8251	·8241	·8231	·8221	·8211	·8202	2	3	5	7	8
35	0·8192	·8181	·8171	·8161	·8151	·8141	·8131	·8121	·8111	·8100	2	3	5	7	8
36	0·8090	·8080	·8070	·8059	·8049	·8039	·8028	·8018	·8007	·7997	2	3	5	7	9
37	0·7986	·7976	·7965	·7955	·7944	·7934	·7923	·7912	·7902	·7891	2	4	5	7	9
38	0·7880	·7869	·7859	·7848	·7837	·7826	·7815	·7804	·7793	·7782	2	4	5	7	9
39	0·7771	·7760	·7749	·7738	·7727	·7716	·7705	·7694	·7683	·7672	2	4	6	7	9
40	0·7660	·7649	·7638	·7627	·7615	·7604	·7593	·7581	·7570	·7559	2	4	6	8	9
41	0·7547	·7536	·7524	·7513	·7501	·7490	·7478	·7466	·7455	·7443	2	4	6	8	10
42	0·7431	·7420	·7408	·7396	·7385	·7373	·7361	·7349	·7337	·7325	2	4	6	8	10
43	0·7314	·7302	·7290	·7278	·7266	·7254	·7242	·7230	·7218	·7206	2	4	6	8	10
44	0·7193	·7181	·7169	·7157	·7145	·7133	·7120	·7108	·7096	·7083	2	4	6	8	10
	0'	6'	12'	18'	24'	30'	36'	42'	48'	54'	1'	2'	3'	4'	5'

NATURAL COSINES

	0′	6′	12′	18′	24′	30′	36′	42′	48′	54′	1′	2′	3′	4′	5′
45°	0·7071	·7059	·7046	·7034	·7022	·7009	·6997	·6984	·6972	·6959	2	4	6	8	10
46	0·6947	·6934	6921	6909	·6896	·6884	·6871	·6858	·6845	·6833	2	4	6	8	11
47	0·6820	6807	·6794	·6782	·6769	·6756	·6743	·6730	6717	·6704	2	4	6	9	11
48	0·6691	·6678	·6665	·6652	·6639	·6626	·6613	6600	·6587	·6574	2	4	6	9	11
49	0 6561	·6547	·6534	·6521	·6508	·6494	·6481	·6468	·6455	·6441	2	4	7	9	11
50	0·6428	·6414	·6401	·6388	·6374	·6361	·6347	·6334	·6320	·6307	2	4	7	9	11
51	0·6293	·6280	·6266	·6252	·6239	·6225	·6211	·6198	·6184	·6170	2	5	7	9	11
52	0·6157	·6143	·6129	·6115	·6101	·6088	·6074	·6060	·6046	·6032	2	5	7	9	12
53	0·6018	·6004	·5990	·5976	·5962	·5948	·5934	·5920	·5906	·5892	2	5	7	9	12
54	0·5878	·5864	·5850	·5835	·5821	·5807	·5793	·5779	·5764	·5750	2	5	7	9	12
55	0·5736	·5721	·5707	·5693	·5678	·5664	·5650	·5635	·5621	5606	2	5	7	10	12
56	0·5592	·5577	·5563	5548	5534	·5519	·5505	·5490	·5476	·5461	2	5	7	10	12
57	0·5446	·5432	·5417	·5402	·5388	·5373	·5358	·5344	·5329	·5314	2	5	7	10	12
58	0·5299	·5284	·5270	·5255	·5240	·5225	·5210	·5195	·5180	·5165	2	5	8	10	12
59	0·5150	·5135	·5120	·5105	·5090	·5075	·5060	5045	·5030	·5015	2	5	8	10	12
60	0·5000	·4985	·4970	·4955	·4939	·4924	4909	·4894	·4879	·4863	3	5	8	10	13
61	0·4848	·4833	·4818	·4802	4787	·4772	·4756	·4741	·4726	·4710	3	5	8	10	13
62	0·4695	·4679	·4664	·4648	4633	·4617	·4602	·4586	·4571	·4555	3	5	8	10	13
63	0·4540	·4524	·4509	·4493	4478	·4462	·4446	·4431	·4415	·4399	3	5	8	10	13
64	0·4384	·4368	·4352	·4337	·4321	·4305	·4289	·4274	·4258	·4242	3	5	8	11	13
65	0·4226	·4210	·4195	·4179	·4163	·4147	·4131	·4115	·4099	·4083	3	5	8	11	13
66	0·4067	·4051	·4035	·4019	4003	·3987	·3971	3955	·3939	·3923	3	5	8	11	13
67	0·3907	3891	3875	3859	3843	3827	·3811	·3795	·3778	·3762	3	5	8	11	13
68	0·3746	3730	·3714	3697	·3681	3665	·3649	·3633	3616	3600	3	5	8	11	14
69	0·3584	3567	·3551	·3535	·3518	·3502	·3486	·3469	3453	·3437	3	5	8	11	14
70	0·3420	·3404	·3387	·3371	·3355	3338	·3322	·3305	·3289	·3272	3	5	8	11	14
71	0·3256	·3239	·3223	·3206	·3190	3173	·3156	·3140	·3123	·3107	3	6	8	11	14
72	0·3090	·3074	·3057	3040	·3024	3007	·2990	·2974	·2957	·2940	3	6	8	11	14
73	0·2924	·2907	·2890	·2874	·2857	·2840	·2823	·2807	·2790	·2773	3	6	8	11	14
74	0·2756	·2740	·2723	·2706	·2689	·2672	·2656	·2639	·2622	·2605	3	6	8	11	14
75	0·2588	·2571	·2554	·2538	·2521	·2504	·2487	·2470	·2453	·2436	3	6	8	11	14
76	0·2419	·2402	·2385	·2368	·2351	·2334	·2317	·2300	·2284	·2267	3	6	8	11	14
77	0·2250	·2232	·2215	·2198	·2181	·2164	·2147	·2130	·2113	·2096	3	6	9	11	14
78	0·2079	·2062	·2045	·2028	·2011	·1994	·1977	·1959	·1942	·1925	3	6	9	11	14
79	0·1908	·1891	·1874	·1857	·1840	·1822	·1805	·1788	·1771	·1754	3	6	9	11	14
80	0·1736	1719	·1702	1685	·1668	·1650	·1633	·1616	·1599	·1582	3	6	9	11	14
81	0·1564	·1547	·1530	·1513	·1495	·1478	·1461	·1444	·1426	1409	3	6	9	11	14
82	0·1392	·1374	·1357	·1340	·1323	·1305	·1288	·1271	·1253	·1236	3	6	9	12	14
83	0·1219	·1201	·1184	·1167	·1149	·1132	·1115	1097	·1080	·1063	3	6	9	12	14
84	0·1045	·1028	·1011	·0993	·0976	·0958	·0941	·0924	·0906	·0889	3	6	9	12	14
85	0·0872	·0854	·0837	·0819	·0802	·0785	·0767	·0750	·0732	·0715	3	6	9	12	14
86	0·0698	·0680	·0663	·0645	·0628	·0610	·0593	·0576	·0558	·0541	3	6	9	12	15
87	0·0523	·0506	0489	·0471	·0454	·0436	·0419	·0401	·0384	·0366	3	6	9	12	15
88	0·0349	·0332	·0314	·0297	·0279	·0262	·0244	·0227	·0209	·0192	3	6	9	12	15
89	0·0175	·0157	·0140	·0122	·0105	·0087	·0070	·0052	·0035	0017	3	6	9	12	15
	0′	6′	12′	18′	24′	30′	36′	42′	48′	54′	1′	2′	3′	4′	5′

Proportional Parts

	0'	6'	12'	18'	24'	30'	36'	42'	48'	54'	1'	2'	3'	4'	5'
0°	0·0000	·0017	·0035	·0052	·0070	·0087	·0105	·0122	·0140	·0157	3	6	9	12	15
1	0·0175	·0192	·0209	·0227	·0244	·0262	·0279	·0297	·0314	·0332	3	6	9	12	15
2	0·0349	·0367	·0384	·0402	·0419	·0437	·0454	·0472	·0489	·0507	3	6	9	12	15
3	0·0524	·0542	·0559	·0577	·0594	·0612	·0629	·0647	·0664	·0682	3	6	9	12	15
4	0·0699	·0717	·0734	·0752	·0769	·0787	·0805	·0822	·0840	·0857	3	6	9	12	15
5	0·0875	·0892	·0910	·0928	·0945	·0963	·0981	·0998	·1016	·1033	3	6	9	12	15
6	0·1051	·1069	·1086	·1104	·1122	·1139	·1157	·1175	·1192	·1210	3	6	9	12	15
7	0·1228	·1246	·1263	·1281	·1299	·1317	·1334	·1352	·1370	·1388	3	6	9	12	15
8	0·1405	·1423	·1441	·1459	·1477	·1495	·1512	·1530	·1548	·1566	3	6	9	12	15
9	0·1584	·1602	·1620	·1638	·1655	1673	·1691	·1709	·1727	·1745	3	6	9	12	15
10	0·1763	·1781	·1799	·1817	·1835	·1853	·1871	·1890	·1908	·1926	3	6	9	12	15
11	0·1944	·1962	·1980	·1998	·2016	·2035	·2053	·2071	·2089	·2107	3	6	9	12	15
12	0·2126	·2144	·2162	·2180	·2199	·2217	·2235	·2254	·2272	·2290	3	6	9	12	15
13	0·2309	·2327	·2345	·2364	·2382	·2401	·2419	·2438	·2456	2475	3	6	9	12	15
14	0·2493	·2512	·2530	·2549	·2568	·2586	·2605	·2623	·2642	·2661	3	6	9	12	16
15	0·2679	·2698	·2717	·2736	·2754	·2773	·2792	·2811	·2830	·2849	3	6	9	13	16
16	0·2867	·2886	·2905	·2924	·2943	·2962	·2981	·3000	·3019	·3038	3	6	9	13	16
17	0·3057	·3076	·3096	·3115	·3134	·3153	·3172	·3191	·3211	·3230	3	6	9	13	16
18	0·3249	·3269	·3288	·3307	·3327	·3346	·3365	·3385	·3404	·3424	3	6	10	13	16
19	0·3443	·3463	·3482	·3502	·3522	·3541	·3561	·3581	·3600	·3620	3	6	10	13	16
20	0·3640	·3659	·3679	·3699	·3719	·3739	·3759	·3779	·3799	3819	3	6	10	13	17
21	0·3839	·3859	·3879	·3899	·3919	·3939	·3959	·3979	·4000	·4020	3	7	10	13	17
22	0·4040	·4061	·4081	·4101	·4122	·4142	·4163	·4183	·4204	·4224	3	7	10	14	17
23	0·4245	·4265	·4286	·4307	·4327	·4348	·4369	·4390	·4411	·4431	3	7	10	14	17
24	0·4452	·4473	·4494	·4515	·4536	·4557	·4578	·4599	·4621	·4642	4	7	11	14	18
25	0·4663	·4684	·4706	·4727	·4748	·4770	·4791	·4813	·4834	·4856	4	7	11	14	18
26	0·4877	·4899	·4921	·4942	·4964	·4986	·5008	·5029	·5051	·5073	4	7	11	15	18
27	0·5095	·5117	·5139	·5161	·5184	·5206	·5228	·5250	·5272	·5295	4	7	11	15	18
28	0·5317	·5339	·5362	·5384	·5407	·5430	·5452	·5475	·5498	·5520	4	8	11	15	19
29	0·5543	·5566	·5589	·5612	·5635	·5658	·5681	·5704	·5727	·5750	4	8	12	15	19
30	0·5774	·5797	·5820	·5844	·5867	·5890	·5914	·5938	·5961	·5985	4	8	12	16	20
31	0·6009	·6032	·6056	·6080	·6104	·6128	·6152	·6176	·6200	·6224	4	8	12	16	20
32	0·6249	·6273	·6297	·6322	·6346	·6371	·6395	·6420	·6445	·6469	4	8	12	16	20
33	0·6494	·6519	·6544	·6569	·6594	·6619	·6644	·6669	·6694	·6720	4	8	13	17	21
34	0·6745	·6771	·6796	·6822	·6847	·6873	·6899	·6924	·6950	·6976	4	9	13	17	21
35	0·7002	·7028	·7054	·7080	·7107	·7133	7159	7186	7212	7239	4	9	13	18	22
36	0·7265	·7292	·7319	·7346	·7373	·7400	·7427	·7454	·7481	7508	5	9	14	18	23
37	0·7536	·7563	·7590	·7618	7646	·7673	·7701	·7729	·7757	7785	5	9	14	18	23
38	0·7813	·7841	·7869	·7898	·7926	·7954	·7983	·8012	·8040	·8069	5	10	14	19	24
39	0·8098	·8127	·8156	·8185	·8214	·8243	·8273	·8302	·8332	·8361	5	10	15	20	24
40	0·8391	·8421	·8451	·8481	8511	·8541	·8571	·8601	·8632	8662	5	10	15	20	25
41	0·8693	·8724	·8754	·8785	·8816	·8847	·8878	·8910	·8941	·8972	5	10	16	21	26
42	0·9004	·9036	·9067	·9099	9131	·9163	·9195	·9228	·9260	9293	5	11	16	21	26
43	0·9325	·9358	·9391	·9424	·9457	·9490	·9523	·9556	·9590	9623	6	11	17	22	28
44	0·9657	·9691	·9725	·9759	·9793	·9827	·9861	·9896	·9930	·9965	6	11	17	23	29
	0'	6'	12'	18'	24'	30'	36'	42'	48'	54'	1'	2'	3'	4'	5'

NATURAL TANGENTS

	0′	6′	12′	18′	24′	30′	36′	42′	48′	54′	1′	2′	3′	4′	5′
45°	1·0000	·0035	·0070	·0105	·0141	·0176	·0212	·0247	·0283	·0319	6	12	18	24	30
46	1·0355	·0392	·0428	·0464	·0501	·0538	·0575	·0612	·0649	·0686	6	12	18	25	31
47	1·0724	·0761	·0799	·0837	·0875	·0913	·0951	·0990	·1028	·1067	6	13	19	25	32
48	1·1106	·1145	·1184	·1224	·1263	·1303	·1343	·1383	·1423	·1463	7	13	20	27	33
49	1·1504	·1544	·1585	·1626	·1667	·1708	·1750	·1792	·1833	·1875	7	14	21	28	34
50	1·1918	·1960	·2002	·2045	·2088	·2131	·2174	·2218	·2261	·2305	7	14	22	29	36
51	1·2349	·2393	·2437	·2482	·2527	·2572	·2617	·2662	·2708	·2753	8	15	23	30	38
52	1·2799	·2846	·2892	·2938	·2985	·3032	·3079	·3127	·3175	·3222	8	16	24	31	39
53	1·3270	·3319	·3367	·3416	·3465	·3514	·3564	·3613	·3663	·3713	8	16	25	33	41
54	1·3764	·3814	3865	·3916	·3968	·4019	·4071	·4124	·4176	·4229	9	17	26	34	43
55	1·4281	4335	·4388	·4442	·4496	·4550	·4605	·4659	·4715	·4770	9	18	27	36	45
56	1·4826	·4882	·4938	·4994	·5051	·5108	·5166	·5224	·5282	·5340	10	19	29	38	48
57	1·5399	·5458	·5517	·5577	·5637	·5697	·5757	·5818	·5880	·5941	10	20	30	40	50
58	1·6003	·6066	·6128	·6191	6255	·6319	·6383	·6447	·6512	·6577	11	21	32	43	53
59	1·6643	·6709	·6775	·6842	·6909	·6977	·7045	·7113	·7182	·7251	11	23	34	45	57
60	1·7321	7391	·7461	7532	·7603	·7675	·7747	·7820	·7893	7966	12	24	36	48	60
61	1·8040	·8115	·8190	·8265	·8341	·8418	·8495	·8572	8650	·8728	13	26	38	51	64
62	1·8807	·8887	·8967	·9047	·9128	·9210	·9292	·9375	·9458	·9542	14	27	41	55	68
63	1·9626	·9711	·9797	·9883	1·9970	2·0057	·0145	·0233	·0323	·0413	15	29	44	58	73
64	2·0503	0594	·0686	·0778	·0872	·0965	·1060	·1155	·1251	·1348	16	31	47	63	78
65	2·145	·154	·164	·174	·184	·194	·204	·215	·225	·236	2	3	5	7	8
66	2·246	·257	267	·278	·289	·300	·311	·322	·333	·344	2	4	5	7	9
67	2·356	·367	·379	391	·402	·414	·426	·438	·450	·463	2	4	6	8	10
68	2·475	·488	·500	·513	526	·539	·552	·565	·578	·592	2	4	6	9	11
69	2·605	·619	633	·646	·660	·675	·689	·703	·718	·733	2	5	7	9	12
70	2·747	·762	778	·793	·808	·824	·840	·856	·872	·888	3	5	8	10	13
71	2·904	·921	·937	·954	971	2·989	3·006	·024	·042	·060	3	6	9	12	14
72	3·078	·096	·115	·133	·152	·172	·191	·211	·230	·251	3	6	10	13	16
73	3·271	·291	312	333	·354	·376	·398	·420	·442	·465	4	7	11	14	18
74	3·487	·511	534	·558	·582	·606	·630	·655	·681	·706	4	8	12	16	20
75	3·732	·758	·785	·812	·839	·867	·895	·923	·952	·981	5	9	14	19	23
76	4·011	·041	071	102	·134	165	·198	·230	·264	·297	5	11	16	21	27
77	4·331	·366	402	·437	·474	·511	·548	·586	·625	·665	6	12	19	25	31
78	4·705	·745	·787	829	·872	·915	4·959	5·005	·050	·097	7	15	22	29	37
79	5·145	·193	·242	·292	·343	·396	·449	·503	·558	·614	9	18	26	35	44
80	5·671	·730	·789	·850	·912	5·976	6·041	107	·174	243	11	21	32	43	54
81	6·314	·386	460	·535	·612	·691	·772	·855	6·940	7·026	13	27	40	54	67
82	7·115	·207	300	396	·495	·596	·700	·806	7·916	8·028	17	34	51	69	86
83	8·144	·264	·386	·513	·643	·777	8·915	9·058	·205	·357	23	46	68	91	114
84	9·514	9·677	9·845	10·019	10·199	10·385	10·579	10·780	10·988	11·205					
85	11·43	11·66	11·91	12·16	12·43	12·71	13·00	13·30	13·62	13·95	p.p. cease				
86	14·30	14·67	15·06	15·46	15·89	16·35	16·83	17·34	17·89	18·46	to be				
87	19·08	19·74	20·45	21·20	22·02	22·90	23·86	24·90	26·03	27·27	sufficiently				
88	28·64	30·14	31·82	33·69	35·80	38·19	40·92	44·07	47·74	52·08	accurate				
89	57·29	63·66	71·62	81·85	95·49	114·6	143·2	191·0	286·5	573·0					
	0′	6′	12′	18′	24′	30′	36′	42′	48′	54′	1′	2′	3′	4′	5′

Other mathematical text-books in the "Teach Yourself" series are listed on page ii of this book. If you want to go still further with your mathematical studies, you are recommended to obtain

NATIONAL CERTIFICATE MATHEMATICS

By

P. ABBOTT, B.A.

Formerly Head of the Mathematics Department and Head Master of the Secondary School, The Polytechnic, Regent Street, W.1

C. E. KERRIDGE, B.Sc.

Formerly Lecturer in Mathematics at The Polytechnic, Regent Street, W.1

H. MARSHALL, B.Sc.

Late Lecturer in Mathematics at The Polytechnic, Regent Street, W.1, and

G. E. MAHON, B.Sc.

Late Senior Lecturer in Mathematics, St. Mary's College, Strawberry Hill, Middlesex, and late Lecturer in Mathematics at The Polytechnic, Regent Street, W.1.

Completely revised by W. E. FISHER, O.B.E., D.Sc.

This three-volume work covers the full course in Mathematics taken by students working at Technical Colleges for the National Certificate, and is particularly well adapted for use by students working privately.

"The work has been carefully adjusted and co-related to the needs and capacities of part-time students and provides for occasional reviews of work done in earlier stages. As a general course in mathematics, these three books offer a sound training up to the application of differential and integral calculus to simple algebraic and trigonometric functions."   *Engineering*

"Well-planned, systematic text-books containing full and detailed explanations of each section of the syllabus. For private students and those taking engineering courses in Technical Institutes, these books are ideal."

Schoolmaster